SIZEWELL B PUBLIC INQUIRY

Report on applications by the Central Electricity Generating Board for

Consent for the construction of a Pressurised Water Reactor and

a Direction that planning permission be deemed to be granted for that development

Inquiry 11 January 1983 — 7 March 1985
Presented to the Secretary of State for Energy on 5 December 1986

Inspector

Sir Frank Layfield, QC.

Assessors

Professor J M Alexander, DSc(Eng), FEng, FIMechE.

Sir Christopher Foster, MA

Professor W B Hall, FEng, FIMechE.

Dr J Vennart CBE, DSc, CPhys, FInstP.

© Crown Copyright 1987
First published 1987

ISBN 0 11 411575 3

CONTENTS

SECTION 8 – THE CASE FOR SIZEWELL B : CAPACITY NEED

Chapters:

SECTION 9 – THE CASE FOR SIZEWELL B : OTHER CONSIDERATIONS

Chapters:

SECTION 10 – CONCLUSIONS ON THE ECONOMIC CASE

Chapter:

SECTION 11 – FUTURE POWER STATION ORDERS

Chapter:

VOLUME 7

PART V – SITE SELECTION AND ENVIRONMENTAL CONSEQUENCES

SECTION 1 – THE SIZEWELL SITE AND ITS SELECTION

Chapters:

SECTION 2 - THE POTENTIAL EFFECTS OF SIZEWELL B ON THE
          ENVIRONMENT

   Chapters:

PART VI - OTHER MATTERS

   Chapters:

PART VII - CONCLUSIONS AND RECOMMENDATIONS

   Chapters:

VOLUME 8

GLOSSARY

INDEX

APPENDICES:

GLOSSARY

The glossary consists of a list of the acronyms and a list
of the major technical terms used in the Report.

ACRONYMS

ACS	average cold spell
ACSNI	Advisory Committee on the Safety of Nuclear Installations
AECB	Atomic Energy Control Board (of Canada)
AEEW	Atomic Energy Establishment Winfrith
AFWS	auxiliary feedwater system
AGR	Advanced Gas-Cooled Reactor
ALARA	as low as reasonably achievable
ALARP	as low as reasonably practicable
ALI	annual limit of intake
ALP	Australian Labour Party
AMR	absolute minimum radius
AONB	Area of Outstanding Natural Beauty
APG	A Power for Good Ltd
ARA	Antwerp/Rotterdam/Amsterdam
ASAW	automatic submerged-arc welding
ASME	American Society of Mechanical Engineers
ASPS	Accident Sequence Precursor Study
ATWT	anticipated transient without trip
AVT	all volatile treatment
AWA	Anglian Water Authority
BAND	Billingham Against Nuclear Dumping
BCUPD	British Civil Uranium Procurement Directorate
BCUPO	British Civil Uranium Procurement Organisation
BDBA	beyond design basis accident
BNFL	British Nuclear Fuels plc
BSI	British Standards Institution
BWR	Boiling Water Reactor
CANDU	Canadian Deuterium Uranium System
CBA	cost benefit analysis
CBI	Confederation of British Industries
CCF	common cause failure
CCWS	component cooling water system
CDFR	Commercial Demonstration Fast Reactor
CEGB	Central Electricity Generating Board
CERG	Cambridge Energy Research Group
CES	Centre for Energy Studies (South Bank Polytechnic)
CFDT	Confederation Francaise Democratique de Travailleurs
CFO	County Fire Officer
CHP	combined heat and power
CIM	Capital Investment Memorandum (CEGB)
CND	Campaign for Nuclear Disarmament
CPE	construction period extension
CPRE	Council for the Protection of Rural England
CSF	critical safety function
CVCS	chemical and volume control system
DBA	design basis accident
DBF	design basis fault
DDT	defect detection trial
DEmp	Department of Employment
DEN	Department of Energy
DH	district heating
DHSS	Department of Health and Social Security
DNA	deoxyribonucleic acid
DNC	declared net capability

DOE	Department of the Environment
DSG	Design Safety Guidelines (CEGB)
DTI	Department of Trade and Industry
dwt	deadweight tonne
DTp	Department of Transport
EAFS	essential auxiliary feedwater system
EBS	emergency boration system
ECC	Electricity Consumers' Council
ECCS	emergency core cooling system
ECGD	Export Credit Guarantee Department
EdF	Electricite de France
EEC	European Economic Community
EEO	Energy Efficiency Office
EFL	external financing limit
EM	evaluation model
EMF	electromagnetic filtration
EPEA	Electrical Power Engineers' Association
ERL	emergency reference level
ESA	employment service area
ESWS	essential service water system
ETP	executive target programme
ETSU	Energy Tehnology Support Unit
EURATOM	European Atomic Energy Community
FEBA	flooding experiments in blocked arrays
FFTF	fast flux test facility
FGD	flue gas desulphurisation
FLECHT	full length emergency cooling heat transfer
fob	free on board
FOE	Friends of the Earth Ltd
FSR	Final Safety Report
GDCD	Generation Development and Construction Division (CEGB)
GDP	gross domestic product
GLC	Greater London Council
GMBATU	General, Municipal, Boilermakers and Allied Trades Union
GoO	Government Interdepartmental Group of Officials
GRS	German Risk Study
GRWS	gaseous radwaste system
GSS	Generation Security Standard
GTA	Government Technical Adviser
GVW	gross vehicle weight
ha	hectare
HFO	heavy fuel oil
HGV	heavy goods vehicle
HHSIS	high head safety injection system
HLW	high-level waste
HNB	High Nuclear Background
HSC	Health and Safety Commission
HSD	Health and Safety Department (CEGB)
HSE	Health and Safety Executive
HTR	High Temperature Reactor
IAEA	International Atomic Energy Agency
ICRP	International Commission on Radiological Protection
IDC	Industrial Development Certificate
IDF	Ipswich Friends of the Earth
IEA	International Energy Agency
IIA	Independent Inspection Agency
ILW	intermediate-level waste

IRR	internal rate of return
IRT	inadvertent reactor trip
IVC	Inspection Validation Centre
JEP	Joint Ecology Parties
JPC	Joint Local Parish Councils
JPT	Joint Project Team
KWU	Kraftwerk Union
LD	lethal dose
LDBF	limiting design basis fault
LER	Licensee Event Report
LET	linear energy transfer
LHSIS	low head safety injection system
LIS	laser isotope separation
LLW	low-level waste
LOBI	loop blowdown investigation
LOCA	loss of coolant accident
LOFT	Loss of Fluid Test
LOTS	LOCA Transient Studies (Committee)
LPA	Local Planning Authorities
LRWS	liquid radwaste system
LTC	Leiston Town Council
LWR	Light Water Reactor
MAFF	Ministry of Agriculture, Fisheries and Food
MCR	main control room
MD	morbidity dose
MDA	Mutual Defence Agreement
MHWOT	mean high water ordinary tide
MMC	Monopolies and Mergers Commission
MNB	Medium Nuclear Background
MOHLG	Ministry of Housing and Local Government
MRC	Medical Research Council
MSC	Manpower Services Commission
MSHA	Mine Safety and Health Administration (US)
MSIV	main steam isolating valve
MSLB	main steam line break
mtce	million tonnes of coal equivalent
mvk	million vehicle kilometres
NAC	net avoidable cost
NAECI	National Agreement for the Engineering Construction Industry
NAIR	National Arrangements for Incidents involving Radioactivity
NCB	National Coal Board
NCC	Nature Conservancy Council
NCLP	Norfolk County Labour Party
NDE	non-destructive examination
NDR	net design rating
NEBR	Nuclear Emergency Briefing Room
NEC	net effective cost
NEDO	National Economic Development Office
NFC	nuclear fuel cycle
NHS	National Health Service
NII	HM Nuclear Installations Inspectorate
NIOSH	National Institute for Occupational Safety and Health (US)
NIREX	Nuclear Industry Radioactive Waste Executive
NNC	National Nuclear Corporation
NNNB	No New Nuclear Background
NNR	National Nature Reserve
NPAB	Nuclear Power Advisory Board

NPT	Non-Proliferation Treaty
NPV	net present value
NRC	Nuclear Regulatory Commission (US)
NRPB	National Radiological Protection Board
NSSS	nuclear steam supply system
NUM	National Union of Mineworkers
NUPE	National Union of Public Employees
OCAW	Oil, Chemical and Atomic Workers' Union (US)
OD	ordnance datum
OECD	Organisation for Economic Co-operation and Development
ONSWG	Operators in Nuclear Safety Working Group (NII)
OPCS	Office of Population Censuses and Surveys
OPEC	Organisation of Petroleum Exporting Countries
OSC	Operational Support Centre
OWC	other works costs
pa	per annum
PCSR	Pre-Construction Safety Report
PISC	Plate Inspection Steering Committee
PMB	Project Management Board
PMT	Project Management Team
PORV	power-operated relief valve
ppm	parts per million
PPS	primary protection system
PRA	probablistic risk assessment
PSBR	public sector borrowing requirement
PVQAB	Pressure Vessel Quality Assurance Board
PWR	Pressurised Water Reactor
QA	quality assurance
RCC	reactor coolant circuit
RCCA	rod cluster control assembly
RCP	reactor coolant pump
REER	real effective exchange rate
RER	real exchange rate
RHRS	residual heat removal system
RIBA	Royal Institute of British Architects
RPE	relative price effect
RPS	reactor protection system
RPV	reactor pressure vessel
RSPB	Royal Society for the Protection of Birds
RSS	Reactor Safety Study (USNRC)
RTZ	Rio Tinto-Zinc Corporation plc
RUHS	reserve ultimate heat sink
RWMAC	Radioactive Waste Management Advisory Committee
RWST	refuelling water storage tank
SAP	Safety Assessment Principles (NII)
SFA	start to finish allowance
SGHWR	Steam Generating Heavy Water Reactor
SGTR	steam generator tube rupture
SNUPPS	Standardised Nuclear Unit Power Plant System
SOI	station operating instruction
SPS	secondary protection system
SPS	Suffolk Preservation Society
SRD	Safety and Reliability Directorate (UKAEA)
SRV	safety relief valve
SSBA	Stop Sizewell B Association and Ecoropa
SSE	safe shut-down earthquake
SSEB	South of Scotland Electricity Board
SSSI	Site of Special Scientific Interest
SWAPO	South West Africa Peoples' Organisation

tce	tonne of coal equivalent
TCPA	Town and Country Planning Association
THORP	Thermal Oxide Reprocessing Plant
TMI	Three Mile Island
TUC	Trades Union Congress
TULA	Anti-PWR Consortium of Trade Unions and Local Authorities
UKAEA	United Kingdom Atomic Energy Authority
UN	United Nations
UNSCEAR	United Nations Scientific Committee on the Effects of Atomic Radiation
UOC	uranium ore concentrate
USNRC	United States Nuclear Regulatory Commission
VDU	visual display unit
WANA	Welsh Anti-Nuclear Alliance
WCAP	Westinghouse's Sizewell B Probabilistic Safety Study, WCAP 9991, Rev 1 (CEGB/S/123)
WDC	Wansbeck District Council
WL	working level
WLM	working level month
YND	South and West Yorkshire, Nottinghamshire and Derbyshire County Councils
ZPPR	Zero Power Plutonium Reactor

GLOSSARY

Absorbed dose. The energy imparted to matter such as tissue per unit mass by ionising radiation. The special name of the SI unit of absorbed dose is the gray (Gy). One gray is equal to one joule of absorbed energy per kilogram.

Accident. A fault or combination of faults with potentially serious consequences.

Accident Probability Analysis. The use of probabilities in combination with the logical analysis of faults and accidents using fault and/or event trees.

Accident Sequence. A combination of faults which occur in a defined chronological order.

Accident Sequence Precursor Study (ASPS). A study of Licensee Event Reports (qv) commissioned by the US Nuclear Regulatory Commission. The objectives of the ASPS were:
   a) to identify faults and accident sequences relatively more likely to lead to a degraded core;
   b) to identify faults and accident sequences which had been poorly modelled or omitted in other probabilistic studies;
   c) to estimate the annual probabilities of faults and the annual probability of a degraded core by alternative means to those used in other probabilistic studies.

Accumulators. Large tanks of borated water, pressurised to 4.5 MPa. One accumulator is connected to each cold leg (qv). If the reactor coolant circuit (RCC) pressure dropped below that of the accumulators, for example following a loss of coolant accident, non-return valves would automatically allow the borated water to flow into the RCC. The accumulators are part of the emergency core cooling system (qv).

Activated Corrosion Products. Particles produced by erosion and corrosion of the inner surface of the reactor coolant circuit which have been irradiated by neutrons and become radioactive.

Activation Products. Radionuclides formed by irradiation of the coolant.

Active. Possessing or pertaining to radioactivity.

Activity. In a given quantity of material, the average number of spontaneous nuclear transformations occurring per unit time. The special name of the SI unit of activity is the becquerel (Bq) (qv).

Actuation System. A system which automatically initiates appropriate safety and support plant and takes other appropriate action following the detection of a fault.

Additive Cut-Off Technique. A method of modelling the effects of common cause failures (qv) in accident probability analysis. First, allowance is made in fault and event tree analysis for all the ways in which a system depends on common support services such as cooling water and electricity. Second, an allowance is added to cover unforeseen common cause failures.

Advanced Gas-Cooled Reactor (AGR). A development of the Calder Hall and early CEGB reactors which operates at higher temperatures and gives greater fuel burn-up. It is being used for the current generation of reactor: the latest design is being built at Heysham II and Torness. The AGR is a reactor having a graphite moderator and carbon dioxide gas as the coolant which uses slightly enriched uranium oxide fuel in stainless steel cans.

ALARA (As Low As Reasonably Achievable). Application of the ALARA principle to risk or radiation dose involves achieving a proper balance between risk and benefit to the community taking cost, social and all other relevant factors into consideration.

ALARP (As Low As Reasonably Practicable). For the purposes of the present Report, ALARP is identical to ALARA.

Alpha Particle. A positively charged particle emitted during the decay of some radioactive nuclei; it is composed of two protons and two neutrons and is identical with the nucleus of the helium-4 atom. Alpha particles are positively charged and are relatively heavy and slow moving. They are able to penetrate only a few tens of millimetres of air and are easily stopped by a sheet of paper. They leave a short dense trail of ionisation in the matter through which they pass and may therefore cause more damage per unit absorbed dose in living tissue than other more penetrative radiation. Nuclei emitting only alpha particles have little biological effect unless they are taken into the body by inhalation or ingestion.

American Society of Mechanical Engineers (ASME) Codes. The ASME Boiler and Pressure Vessel Code is the principal document on which the design of the pressure circuits of water reactor power plants is based, and it is the foundation for the Sizewell B reactor pressure vessel.

Annual Limit on Intake (ALI). A limit imposed on the amount of a radionuclide ingested or inhaled in order to ensure compliance with dose limits for both non-stochastic and stochastic effects of radiation. It is measured in becquerel (Bq) (qv).

Annuitised Capital Charge. The conversion of a capital cost to a constant annual amount over the life of an investment so that the annual amounts add up to the capital cost when they are discounted at the appropriate discount rate.

Appendix K Criteria. A set of rules and limits for the analysis of loss of coolant accidents (LOCAs) which have regulatory status in the US. The Criteria are intended to ensure that LOCA analyses are pessimistic. A model which complies with Appendix K is known as an Evaluation Model.

Area Board. One of twelve statutory Boards in England and Wales which purchase electricity in bulk from the CEGB and through their distribution systems supply electricity to consumers.

Arithmetic Mean. The arithmetic mean is the total sum of individual values in a data set divided by the number of values in that data set. The mean (or 'average') value is influenced by the actual value of each member of the data set, so that a particularly high or low value can have a noticeable effect.

Assessment Levels. Levels set by the NII which are intended to represent a level of safety at which it is not normally worth the nuclear inspectors undertaking detailed work to examine whether further improvements are reasonably practicable.

Auxiliary Building. The building immediately outside the primary containment which houses supporting services for the reactor.

Auxiliary Feedwater System. An alternative means of providing feedwater (qv) to the steam generators, in case the main feedwater system fails.

Auxiliary Shutdown Room. A room from which the reactor could be shut down safely in the event that the main control room became uninhabitable.

Availability. The extent to which in any specified period an item of plant is in a state to provide the service for which it was designed. It is normally expressed as a percentage; for example, annual availability is the percentage of a year for which plant is available. (See also breakdown and peak availability).

Average Cold Spell (ACS). A spell of cold weather of average severity. Since electricity demand varies with the severity of weather conditions, historic values of winter peak electricity demand are corrected to ACS conditions by a statistical analysis of past weather data and the variation in demand caused by the weather.

Average Cold Spell Demand. The electricity demand which is estimated to occur during a spell of cold weather of average severity.

BART. A computer code which models the ballooning and cooling of a group of identical fuel rods during reflood in a large LOCA.

Base Load. The lowest load continuously supplied by an electrical system over a period of time, normally a year.

Base-Load Operation. A plant or power station having a high availability is said to be operating on base-load when it is operating at full output for as long as it is available in the year.

Becquerel (Bq). A measure of the activity (qv) of a radionuclide. One becquerel is one transformation (or decay) per second.

Benefit-Cost Ratio. The ratio of discounted benefits to discounted costs.

Best Estimate. When used in connection with the analysis of a fault, it means that the analysis has used a mathematical model, assumptions and data which give the most realistic practicable description of the physical processes and parameters (qv) following the fault. The results of such an analysis would be expected to provide the most accurate description of the fault or the consequences of the fault.

Beta Factor Method. A method of modelling the effects of common cause failures (qv) in accident probability analysis. The ratio of common cause failures of an item of equipment to all failures of that item is assumed to be constant, represented by a factor [beta]. Hence the probability of a common cause failure is [beta]p where p is the total failure rate for one single component under consideration.

Beta Particle. An electron emitted in radioactive transformation (or decay). An electron is an elementary particle carrying one unit of negative electric charge. Beta particles can be stopped by a few millimetres of plastic but are of particular danger if taken into or onto the surface of the body.

Bilateral Exchange Rate. The exchange rate of a given currency expressed in terms of a single other currency.

Bleed and Feed. A means of removing heat from the reactor core which does not depend on the steam generators. Reactor coolant is allowed to escape from the reactor coolant circuit through pressuriser PORVs, removing heat with it; the lost coolant is replaced by means of the high head safety injection system.

Blowdown. The initial period of a large LOCA during which the pressure in the reactor coolant circuit falls.

Breakdown Availability. The mean availability achieved during periods when it was intended to operate a plant continuously.

Brittle. The property of being unable to accommodate stresses by localised plastic distortion. Brittle materials have a low fracture toughness (qv). Steel will behave in a brittle manner below a transition temperature which depends on its composition and history.

Burn-up. The amount of fissile material in a reactor which is destroyed by fission or neutron capture expressed as a percentage of the original quantity of fissile material present. Alternatively, the heat obtained per unit mass of fuel, expressed generally as MWd/te.

Bypass. The phenomenon, which may occur in the later part of blowdown (qv) during a large LOCA, that water from the accumulators (qv) is prevented from flowing down the downcomer (qv) by steam flowing in the opposite direction. Consequently the water from the accumulators is forced to flow around the top of the downcomer and out through the broken leg.

CANDU. A Canadian developed nuclear power reactor system. The name is derived from Canada Deuterium Uranium, indicating that the moderator is heavy water and the fuel natural uranium.

Capacity Need. The need for new generating capacity to meet a shortfall between projections of restricted winter maximum demand and future generating capacity on the system.

Central Estimate. The value of a variable such that there is broadly a 50% chance of achieving the value or a higher figure and a 50% chance of achieving that or a lower figure.

Chain Reaction. A nuclear reaction that initiates its own repetition. In nuclear fission, a neutron induces a nucleus to fission as the result of which neutrons are released which cause another nucleus to fission and so on.

Chemical and Volume Control Sytem. A system which continuously extracts, processes and returns a small quantity of reactor coolant in order to:
a) adjust the volume of coolant in the reactor coolant circuit;
b) control the purity of the coolant;
c) adjust the boron concentration to control reactivity.

Cladding.
a) In the case of nuclear fuel, the thin layer, usually of metal, which covers a solid fuel element to prevent the escape of fission products, to prevent corrosion of the fuel element by the coolant and to provide structural support.
b) In the case of a reactor component, a layer of material applied to its surface to provide protection from a hostile environment. For example the stainless steel cladding on the inside of the PWR reactor pressure vessel.

Code. A computer program. A computer model will often comprise a number of interacting codes.

Cognitive Errors. Errors involving misinterpretation or misunderstanding.

Cold Leg. The pipe from which reactor coolant enters the reactor pressure vessel.

Cold Overpressurisation. An increase in pressure, for example in the reactor coolant circuit, to above design or safety levels when at a temperature sufficiently low that the material put under stress is brittle (qv).

Collective Dose Equivalent. The sum of the dose equivalents received by all members of a population, measured in man-sievert. The collective dose equivalent is useful in considering the social risk arising from a source of radiation.

Combined Heat and Power (CHP). Because of thermodynamic limitations on converting heat into work, about two-thirds of the heat produced by fuel in a power station is discharged as low grade heat in cooling water, the remaining third being converted to electricty. A power station which is designed or converted so that a reasonable quantity of this heat is upgraded for use in industry or for district heating (DH) is known as a CHP power station.

Commissioning. The process during which a plant, having been constructed, is made operational and is confirmed (by, for example, specific acceptance tests) to be in accordance with design assumptions and to have met the performance criteria.

Committed Dose Equivalent. The dose equivalent accumulated in an organ or tissue over a period of 50 years after intake of a radionuclide into the body; it is measured in sievert. Estimates of committed dose equivalent are used to determine limits on the intake of radionuclides by radiation workers.

Common Cause Failure. A failure in which two or more components or systems fail because of common features or factors on which they are dependent or which influence them. The failure modes of the components or systems are not necessarily identical and may arise from failures in the components or systems themselves or from the effects of external influences.

Component. An item of equipment such as a valve or pump.

Component Cooling Water System. A system which provides cooling water for plant items such as heat exchangers, pump seals and equipment room coolers.

Construction Period Extension (CPE). The period added by the CEGB to its target construction time for new generating plant to allow for any optimism in the target time.

Containment. Part of the structure of some nuclear stations: see 'primary containment' and 'secondary containment'.

Containment Bypass.
a) A release of radioactive materials resulting from a failure to isolate the containment or a failure to keep containment temperatures and pressures within design safety limits, following an accidental discharge of reactor coolant
b) A direct discharge of radioactive materials from the reactor outside the containment, for example through the residual heat removal system.

12

Contamination. The existence of radioactive material in any place where it is not desired, particularly where its presence may be be harmful. The material may be liquid or particulate in form.

Contamination Zone. A controlled zone in which the control is imposed in respect of contamination.

Controlled Zone. An area into which the access of personnel is controlled for the purpose of controlling radiation exposure. A controlled zone may be divided into various radiation or contamination zones dependent on the nature of the potential hazard.

Control Rod. A rod used to control the reactivity (qv) of a reactor by the absorption of neutrons. Movement of the rod enables the power level to be held constant or to be varied as required. In the Sizewell B design there are 53 Rod Control Cluster Assemblies (RCCAs), each of which contains 24 individual rods of a silver-indium-cadmium alloy. The expression 'control rod' is often used in place of RCCA.

Coolant (or Cooling) Loop. A circuit in which coolant is pumped from the reactor, where it has been heated, to a heat exchanger, where some of its heat is removed, and back to the reactor for reheating.

Co-processing. The practice of reprocessing spent fuel from civil reactors, which is subject to international safeguards agreements, together with fuel from military reactors, which is unsafeguarded.

Core. That portion of a nuclear reactor containing the fissile material. Sometimes used also to include moderator and support structures.

Cost of Deferment. The effect on the net present value of future costs and savings of deferring an investment project by one year, expressed in £ million.

Critical. Of a nuclear reactor, the condition when it is just capable of sustaining a chain reaction. A reactor is said to be sub-critical when it can no longer sustain such a reaction and super-critical when it is more than capable of just sustaining such a reaction.

Critical Crack Size. A size of crack which, if exceeded, may extend and cause rapid failure of the structure containing the crack.

Critical Group. Those people who receive the maximum total dose, via all pathways, from a particular radiation source.

13

Critical Safety Functions. If the values of critical safety functions (CSFs) are within certain limits, the operator can be satisfied that the plant is in a safe condition. CSFs might include:
a) core heat removal;
b) reactor coolant circuit pressure;
c) core reactivity;
d) reactor coolant circuit inventory;
e) reactor coolant circuit heat removal;
f) containment temperature and pressure;
g) containment isolation.

Crud. Particles produced by erosion and corrosion of the inner surface of the reactor coolant circuit.

dB(A). A measure of noise level, in decibels with 'A' weighting. The 'A' weighting is derived from an electronic filter which reduces the effect of noises of very low and very high frequency; it is intended to give a measure consistent with the subjective rating of many noise sources.

Decay, Radioactive. The decrease in activity of a radioactive material as it transforms spontaneously from one nuclide into another or into a different energy state of the same nuclide. Radioactive decay is usually accompanied by the emission of charged particles and gamma rays. Sometimes used synonymously with radioactive transformation (qv).

Decay Heat. The heat produced by the decay of radioactive nuclides, for example in a shutdown reactor or in fuel removed from a reactor.

Decay Product. A nuclide which results from radioactive decay. Decay products may or may not decay further.

Declared Net Capability (DNC). The maximum sent-out output of a power station taking into account any operational restrictions which would permanently change the output from that originally designed.

Decommissioning. Taking a power station out of normal service either for final disposal or for putting into reserve. In the case of a nuclear power station the term is extended to cover all stages of returning the site to other use.

Degraded Core. A core which has substantially deformed or melted so that adequate cooling may no longer be possible.

Degraded Core Analysis. The systematic analysis of the probability and consequences of those accidents which involve degraded cores.

Design Basis. A statement of the required physical performance limitations and working conditions for a component or system.

Design Basis Accident. An accident which has been taken into account in the design and for which safeguards systems are provided to prevent a degraded core or an unacceptable release of radioactive materials to the environment.

Design Basis Fault. The most serious accident sequences within the design basis in which all the safety systems worked as intended were defined by the CEGB as design basis faults.

Design Rating. The output which a plant is designed to produce (usually measured in MW or GW).

Discount Rate. The annual rate, expressed as a percentage, used to bring the monetary values of a stream of cash flows (costs and benefits) to a common base year.

Diversity. The provision of different types of safety equipment to perform the same safety task, in order to protect against failure of a whole set of redundant (qv) safety equipment for a common reason (for example because they all depend on electrical power, which might fail).

Dose Equivalent. At the point of interest in tissue is the product of the absorbed dose (qv), quality factor (qv) and other modifying factors necessary to obtain an evaluation of the effects of irradiation received by exposed persons, so that the different characteristics of the exposure are taken into account. The special SI unit of dose equivalent is the sievert (Sv).

Downcomer. The annular space between the inside surface of the reactor pressure vessel and the barrel which contains the core. Reactor coolant flows down the downcomer before passing up through the core.

Ductile. The property of being able to accommodate stresses by localised plastic distortion. Ductile materials have a high fracture toughness (qv). Steel will behave in a ductile manner above a transition temperature which depends on its composition and history.

Early Effects. Effects, such as vomiting and death, which occur within a few weeks of exposure to a high level of irradiation. Such levels of irradiation might arise from a large release of radioactive materials from a nuclear reactor.

Eccentricity. The displacement of a fuel pellet from a central position within the fuel clad. The eccentricity varies from zero, for a pellet positioned centrally in the clad, to one, for a pellet touching the cladding.

Effective Dose Equivalent. The quantity obtained by multiplying the dose equivalents to various tissues and organs by the risk weighting factor (qv) appropriate to each and summing the products. It is expressed in sievert.

Effective Exchange Rate. An average trade-weighted exchange rate, measuring the movement of a given currency against a basket of other currencies. It may be expressed either as an index or denominated in a chosen currency.

Electricity Council. The body responsible for co-ordinating the activities of the electricity supply industry.

15

Electromagnetic Filtration. Magnetic filters which remove crud from the reactor coolant, and consequently reduce radiation doses to workers.

Emergency Boration System. A diverse means of shutting down the reactor: boric acid solution is rapidly injected into the reactor coolant if the control rods do not enter the core following a trip signal (boron is a good absorber of neutrons).

Emergency Core Cooling System (ECCS). A system intended to keep the core adequately cooled in the event of a loss of coolant accident. The ECCS has three components:
a) accumulators (qv);
b) a high head safety injection system (qv);
c) a low head safety injection system (qv).

Emergency Reference Levels (ERLs). Values of dose equivalent at which the National Radiological Protection Board recommends that consideration be given to particular countermeasures to limit further exposure.

Enrichment. The process of increasing the number of fissile atoms in nuclear fuel above that occurring in the natural material. It is also the term used to denote the fraction of fissile isotope to the total isotopes present in the material. For example, a material having an enrichment of 3% contians 3% uranium-235 and 97% uranium-238. Natural uranium contains 0.711% uranium-235.

Evaluation Model. A set of computer codes for LOCA analysis which complies with the US Appendix K (qv) regulatory requirements. An Evaluation Model is designed to give pessimistic results.

Event Tree. A logic diagram used to illustrate the alternative courses of events that could follow an initiating fault.

Expressed Preference. The evaluation of public attitudes to risk by means of opinion surveys. People are given statistics and information about the risks posed by a particular activity and asked whether certain risks are or are not tolerable.

Fast Reactor. A nuclear reactor in which no moderator is used to slow down the neutrons. A high concentration of fissile material (usually plutonium) is required.

Fault. Any unplanned departure from the specified function of a system or component because of malfunction, maloperation or defect.

Fault Sequence. See 'accident sequence'.

Fault Tree. A diagram representing the way possible equipment failures can lead to failure to achieve a particular objective such as adequate cooling of the fuel following an initiating fault.

16

Feedwater. The water, previously treated to remove air and impurities, that is supplied to a boiler for evaporation.

Film Boiling. A type of boiling which causes the production of an insulation vapour layer which keeps the coolant from the hot surface that is being cooled, such as the cladding of a fuel rod.

Firm Power. The amount of capacity that a plant or station can be relied on to provide at the time of system maximum demand, taking account of the probability of unplanned outage.

Fissile.
a) Of a nuclide, capable of undergoing fission by neutrons.
b) Of a material, containing one or more fissile nuclides.

Fission. The splitting of a heavy nucleus into two or more parts accompanied by the release of energy and further neutrons. It may occur spontaneously or be induced by the capture of bombarding particles, particularly neutrons.

Fission Products. The nuclides produced in fission, either directly or by the radioactive transformation (or decay) of the fission fragments. Over 300 stable and radioactive fission products have been identified. They represent isotopes of some 35 different chemical elements ranging from arsenic-85 to gadolinium-160.

Flue Gas Desulphurisation. The process by which the sulphur dioxide content of combustion gases from coal-fired plant is reduced in order to control sulphur emissions.

Fracture Toughness. The resistance of a material to the propagation of cracks.

Frequency. The mean number of occurrences per unit time. The interval between occurrences may not be uniform.

Fuel Assembly. An assembly of fuel rods and supporting mechanisms.

Fuel Clad. See 'cladding', part (a).

Fuel Clad Ballooning. The swelling of fuel cladding when subjected to a net internal pressure. Zircaloy fuel cladding is weak and ductile at around 800°C and may balloon at such temperatures. Extensive ballooning, particularly if it occurred on neighbouring rods, would reduce the space available for coolant to flow through the core. As a result, heat removal could be reduced, leading to a higher peak clad temperature.

Fuel Rod. A metal tube containing nuclear fuel. In Sizewell B the metal tube is made of Zircaloy, and the nuclear fuel comprises pellets of enriched uranium dioxide.

Fuel Storage Pond. A large container, ususally made of concrete lined with steel, filled with water in which spent fuel is stored after its removal from the reactor. Fuel is stored in this way until its activity has decayed to the desired level and it can be removed from the site. The water acts as a coolant and a radiation shield.

Gamma Rays. Electromagnetic radiation, similar to X-rays but usually of shorter wavelength, emitted by a nucleus. Each emission is the result of a transition between two energy levels of the nucleus. Gamma rays are usually exceedingly penetrating.

Generating Security Standard (GSS). A measure of the risk of disruption of consumers' electricity supply arising from shortage of generating capacity. At the time of the Inquiry it was defined as meeting in full, without voltage or frequency reductions, demand at the winter peak half-hour in all except 23 winters per century, and avoiding disconnections in all except 3 winters per century.

Gray (Gy). The special name of the SI unit of absorbed dose (qv). One gray is equal to one joule of absorbed energy per kilogram.

Grid. See 'transmission system'.

Guide Tubes. Tubes, included in each fuel assembly, which may be used for control rods.

Half-life. The time taken for the activity of a radionuclide to lose half its value by decay. Each radionuclide has a unique half-life which does not change over time or with physical conditions.

Hazard. Broadly, an occurrence that threatens the safety of the plant which does not result directly from the malfunction of a plant item. Hazards may be internal or external. Internal hazards are those, such as fire, which originate on the site. External hazards are those, such as earthquake, which originate off the site.

Health Physics. The branch of physics concerned with the effects of ionising radiation on living matter and the protection of personnel from the harmful effects of such radiation.

Healthy Worker Effect. The propensity of workers to have a lower mortality rate than the population from which they are drawn, other things being equal. The effect results from the fact that people who are less healthy are less likely to be selected to be workers.

Heat Exchanger. A piece of equipment that transfers heat from one medium to another. A typical example is a steam generator in a PWR in which heat is transferred from the reactor coolant and used to convert water into steam to run the turbine.

18

High Head Safety Injection System (HHSIS). A system which pumps water into each of the four cold legs when the reactor coolant circuit pressure falls below 12.5 MPa. The HHSIS is part of the Emergency Core Cooling System (qv).

High Level Waste. Radioactive waste which requires the heat of radioactive decay to be taken into account in the design of storage or disposal facilities.

Hot Leg. A pipe through which water leaves the reactor pressure vessel and flows to a steam generator.

Identified Operating Instructions. Instructions which, if followed, should ensure that Operating Rules (qv) are not breached. Compliance with Identified Operating Instructions is mandatory.

'Incredible'. The CEGB regards an initiating fault as 'incredible' if
a) 'adequate forewarning of the events which may lead to the accident can be guaranteed and adequate preventive action can be demonstrated;
b) the frequency can be proved to be less than 10^{-7} per reactor year; or
c) it can be discounted by engineering judgment based on appropriate preventive measures'.

Independent Inspection Agency (IIA). A body responsible for certifying that the reactor pressure vessel and certain other components comply with the relevant American Society of Mechanical Engineers Codes (qv) and other requirements. In the case of Sizewell B, Lloyd's Register of Shipping has been contracted as the IIA.

Individual Risk. The annual probability of a specified type or types of harm occurring to a specified individual.

Initiating Event. See 'initiating fault'.

Initiating Fault. A postulated single fault taken as the starting point for an accident sequence. It may not necessarily be the original cause of the accident but may itself be the result of some other cause, such as a hazard (qv).

Integral Design. A reactor pressure vessel design in which the shell flange and nozzle ring are made of a single forging.

Integral Test. An experiment in which interactions between different phenomena and different plant items, for example in a loss of coolant accident, are represented.

Intermediate Level Waste. Radioactive waste with levels of activity exceeding the limits for low level waste (qv), but not requiring the heat generated by radioactive decay to be taken into account in the design of storage or disposal facilities.

Internal Rate of Return. The discount rate at which the net present value of costs and benefits is zero.

Interruptible Demand. The level of demand reduction (measured in MW or GW) which may be achieved through suspending supplies to customers by prior arrangment.

Ion. An elementary particle, atom or molecule that has lost or gained one or more electrons and therefore possesses a net positive or negative charge.

Ionising Radiation. Any radiation (qv) with sufficient energy to ionise matter through which it travels.

Isotopes. Species of an atom with the same number of protons in their nuclei, hence having the same atomic number and belonging to the same element, but differing in the number of neutrons and hence in mass numbers. Such atoms have identical chemical properties but their nuclear characteristics, such as neutron absorption or fissile properties, may be vastly different.

Iteration.
a) Of a mathematical calculation, to find a solution by successive approximation.
b) Of nuclear licensing, the process of submissions, questions and discussions, principally between the NII and CEGB, the object of which was to resolve issues for the purpose of licensing.

L_{10}. The noise level which is exceeded for 10% of the period of time under consideration. This quantity is taken to be a measure of the higher levels of noise occurring in a given time period.

L_{90}. The noise level which is exceeded for 90% of the time. This quantity is regarded as the background noise and is so defined in BS4142.

Late Effects. Those health effects of irradiation, such as cancer and hereditary effects, which are not observed for several years after exposure.

Lethal Dose. The dose which will cause early death; the lethal dose varies between different organs and tissues, and between different individuals. The dose that is expected on average to kill a given percentage of people can be broadly determined: that dose which is expected to kill 50% of the exposed population is known as LD_{50}. It is possible to estimate a threshold dose below which there should be no early deaths.

Licensee Event Report (LER). US licensees of nuclear power stations have to send an LER to the Nuclear Regulatory Commission following any safety-related fault.

Limiting Design Basis Fault. An accident sequence, including an initiating fault and some subsequent specified safety system failures, which has been selected by virtue of its severity to 'bound' other accident sequences.

Linear Energy Transfer. The loss of energy per unit length along the path of a charged particle.

Load. In electricity generation and supply load refers to the instantaneous level of demand (usually measured in MW or GW). In practice, it is measured by reference to the energy supplied over a short period, normally half an hour.

Load Curve. A representation of the variation in demand over a period of time. For example, the daily load curve shows the variation in demand over 24 hours.

Load Factor. For a generating plant, the load factor is the ratio of the kWh actually generated over a period of time, to those which would have been generated if the plant had worked continuously at full output for the period. The load factor of an electricity system as a whole is the ratio of the kWh supplied by that system over a period, normally a year, to the number of kWh which would have been supplied if the highest load in the period had been maintained over that period.

Load Management. The ability to reduce the load supplied to specific consumers on receipt of a signal from their electricity supplier, implemented under the terms of an agreement between supplier and consumer.

Local Liaison Committee. A committee chaired by the power station manager which includes representatives of the police and the district council.

Logic Array. A device which can combine signals using simple logic and issue instructions appropriate to the signals it has received, for example to actuate particular safety systems.

Loss of Coolant Accident (LOCA). An accident in which coolant escapes from the reactor coolant circuit. A LOCA may result from a number of causes, such as a pipe rupture, the failure of a valve to close or leakage at a seal.

Low Head Safety Injection System (LHSIS). A system which pumps water into each of the four cold legs when the reactor coolant circuit pressure falls below 1.7MPa. The LHSIS is part of the emergency core cooling system (qv).

Low Level Waste. Waste containing radioactive materials not exceeding 4 GBq/tonne alpha-activity or 12 GBq/tonne beta and gamma-activity, but which does not qualify for disposal as ordinary non-radioactive refuse.

Lower Head. The hemispherical dome at the bottom of the reactor pressure vessel.

Lower Plenum. The region in the bottom of the reactor pressure vessel, below the core.

Magnox Reactor. One of the first types of reactor to be used for large-scale production of electricity. The Magnox Reactor uses natural uranium as fuel, graphite as the moderator and carbon dioxide gas under pressure as the coolant. It is so called because of the use of magnesium in the fuel cladding.

Main Steam Isolation Valve. A valve in each of the four main steam lines (qv) which is designed to shut rapidly and limit the steam leakage if the main steam line were to fail.

Main Steam Line. The pipe through which steam flows from the steam generator to the main steam header in the turbine hall.

Man-Sievert (Man-Sv). The unit of collective dose equivalent (qv).

Maximum Annual Demand. The highest, or peak, demand during a year.

Megawatt-Days per Tonne (MWd/te). A unit used for expressing the heat output per tonne of fuel in a reactor, and hence the burn-up. Thus in a reactor with 100 tonnes of fuel, operating at 150 MW (thermal) for a year, the fuel is irradiated at an average of (365 x 150)/100=547.5 MWd/te.

Merit Order. Each generating unit on an interconnected electricity supply system will have different avoidable costs of generation. The merit order is a list of all such units on the system in order of increasing avoidable costs. Not all generating units are needed all the time so those lower on the merit order (those with higher avoidable costs) are only brought into use at times of high demand while those higher in the merit order (those with lower generating costs) will be used continuously, that is they will be run on base-load operation. This method of running the system is known as merit order operation.

Missiles. Solid objects travelling at high speed. Missiles might arise, for example, from the disruptive failure of pressurised plant.

Model. A theoretical construct which represents aspects of plant behaviour in mathematical terms.

Moderator. A material use in a thermal reactor to reduce the energies of the neutrons from the high value with which they are released in the fission process in order to increase the chances of further fission. The neutrons are slowed down by means of scattering collisions with the nuclei of the moderator. Typical moderator materials are water and graphite.

Morbidity Dose. The dose which will cause a given non-stochastic (qv) effect, such as vomiting; the morbidity dose varies between different effects, between different organs and tissues, and between different individuals. The dose that is expected on average to cause a particular effect in a given percentage of people can be broadly determined: that dose which is expected to cause the effect in 50% of the exposed population is known as MD_{50}. It is possible to estimate a threshold dose below which there should be no effects.

Natural Circulation. In the reactor coolant circuit, a flow of coolant through the coolant loops induced by the density differences between coolant in the hotter and colder parts of the system.

Net Avoidable Cost (NAC). The net cost of keeping plant in service as against retiring it or putting it into reserve. It is expressed as an average annual cost per kW of capacity.

Net Design Rating (NDR). The maximum amount of power that a power station is designed to deliver continuously, after deducting that used on the site or lost in transforming the power to the correct voltage for transmission. It is normally expressed in MW sent out (MWso).

Net Effective Cost. The annuitised net present value of the change in total system costs from building and operating a new power station over its lifetime. It is expressed in £ per kW per annum. A negative NEC indicates that the additional costs of the station are outweighed by cost savings elsewhere on the system.

Net Present Value (NPV). The sum of all cash flows relating to a project brought to a single point of time by means of a discount rate.

Neutron. An uncharged particle with a mass nearly equal to that of a proton and found in the nucleus of every atom heavier than hydrogen.

Node. In computer modelling, a small volume in which each of the relevent properties is represented by a single numerical value based on the average of that property over the volume. The equations solved by the computer are usually simple arithmetical balances relating properties in adjacent nodes.

Non-Destructive Examination. A method for determining the existence and extent of possible defects in a component without damaging the component.

Non-stochastic. When used in relation to the effects of radiation, it describes effects in which the severity of the effect varies with the dose and for which there may be a threshold of dose below which the effect is not observed at all.

Nuclear Fuel Cycle. The sequence of steps, including mining, enrichment, fabrication, utilisation, reprocessing and waste disposal through which nuclear fuel may pass.

Nuclear Steam Supply System. That part of a nuclear power station which produces steam for driving the turbine-generators. In a PWR, the nuclear steam supply system consists of the reactor, the reactor pressure vessel, the reactor coolant circuit and pumps, the steam generators, and the associated auxiliary systems.

Nucleate Boiling. A mode of heat transfer between a solid surface and a liquid, in which vapour bubbles are formed at nuclei (usually small cavities) on the surface of the solid. The bubbles subsequently detach and are replaced by new bubbles.

Nucleus. The positively charged central part of an atom, constituting its main mass.

Operating Rules. A set of mandatory requirements which are prepared by the CEGB for each of its nuclear power stations as a condition of the nuclear site licence: these rules cover the way in which operating parameters and items of plant affecting nuclear safety shall be controlled. Operating Rules are subject to approval by the Nuclear Installations Inspectorate.

Operating Savings. The savings in system running costs resulting from operating a new plant in order of merit and so displacing old plant with higher running costs.

Operational Support Centre (OSC). The administrative centre for off-site actions in the event of an emergency at a CEGB nuclear power station. The OSC would be at a prearranged location between 10 and 30 km from the station.

Opportunity Cost. The value of a resource in its best alternative use.

Optimal Plant Mix. The mixture of generating plant on the system which yields the lowest cost electricity subject to the standards of supply.

Outage. Planned outage is the shutdown of plant for inspection, maintenance, etc. Unplanned outage is the shutdown of plant through breakdown.

Parameter. A quantity in a mathematical equation which can take different values, and which will therefore influence the relationship between dependent and independent variables.

Pathway. A route by which radioactive materials might irradiate people. For example, liquid discharges from a nuclear power station to the sea might increase levels of activity in fish, which might subsequently be consumed by people. Such people would be internally irradiated as a result.

Peak Availability. The availability of plant at times of system maximum demand, taking account only of the probability of unplanned outage.

Pessimism. In safety analysis, the use of assumptions and methods which correspond to a more dangerous situation than that which is likely in reality. By the use of pessimism, additional safety margins can be provided to accommodate any unforeseen or unquantifiable effects which might reduce safety.

Planning Background. The assumptions made about the capacity and type of plant on the generating system in each future year over the lifetime of a new power station.

Planning Margin. The percentage of additional generating plant planned to be in service in the planning years over and above the forecast peak demand to be met by the CEGB in order to meet the generating security standard. It takes account of the expected average availability of generating plant and variations in plant availability, weather conditions and demand forecasts.

Planning Years. In the context of plant and load forecasting the period 7-9 years ahead, being the period required to constuct major new plant.

Potassium Iodate Tablets. Tablets which, if ingested, reduce the risk from inhaling or ingesting radioactive iodine. Iodine accumulates in the thyroid, causing a particular risk of thyroid cancer. Potassium iodate tablets contain stable (ie non-radioactive) iodine; if the thyroid is already saturated with stable iodine from potassium iodate tablets, any radioactive iodine which is ingested or inhaled is less likely to be retained in the body.

Power-Operated Relief Valves. Valves which are operated mechanically or electrically in response to signals; the signals may be sent manually or by the station control system.

Pressurised Thermal Shock. A relatively quick reduction in temperature, causing thermal stresses, while at high pressure.

Pressuriser. A cylindrical vessel with hemispherical ends connected to one of the hot legs in the reactor coolant circuit. The function of the pressuriser is to control changes in the pressure of the reactor coolant circuit.

Primary Containment. In the PWR, a large thick reinforced or prestressed concrete or steel enclosure surrounding the reactor system which is capable of withstanding the pressures and temperatures caused by a loss of coolant accident. It limits the release of fission products to the environment.

Probability.
a) An expected future average rate of occurrence expressed per unit time.
b) The expected average fraction of the total number of demands which will give rise to a particular outcome.

Prompt Dose. A dose received over a very short period (eg a few minutes). A prompt dose is more damaging than a dose received over a longer period.

Protection System. The system which encompasses all electricl and mechanical devices and circuitry involved in generating the signals needed to initiate those actions which are needed after a fault to limit and mitigate its consequences.

Quality Assurance. Planned and systematic actions intended to provide adequate confidence that the general design intention is met, that significant shortcomings are detected and corrected, and that each item or facility will perform satisfactorily in service.

Quality Control. Quality assurance actions which provide a means of control and measure the characteristics of an item, process or facility in accordance with established requirements.

Quality Factor. A factor related to linear energy transfer (qv) which expresses the biological effectiveness of different kinds of radiation. It is used to calculate dose equivalent.

Radiation Zone. A controlled zone (qv) in which the control is imposed in respect of radiation.

Radiation.
a) In nuclear physics, the term embraces electromagnetic waves (X-rays and gamma-rays) and fast-moving particles (alpha particles, electrons, neutrons etc).
b) It may also be used in reactor technology in relation to heat radiation.

Radioactive. A radioactive atom is one which is unstable and undergoes spontaneous transformation (or decay) into another atom. The process is accompanied by the emission of radiation. A radioactive substance is one containing radioactive atoms.

Radioactivity. The property possessed by radioactive (qv) atoms or substances.

Radionuclide. An unstable atom which emits ionising radiation.

Reactivity. A measure of the departure of the reactor from the critical condition. Positive values of the reactivity imply increasing power and negative values decreasing power.

Reactor Cavity. The cavity in the containment floor directly below the reactor pressure vessel.

Reactor Coolant Circuit. The main cooling circuit of the reactor, which removes heat from the core.

Reactor Coolant Pumps. Pumps in the reactor coolant circuit between each steam generator and each cold leg, which pump water around the circuit.

Reactor Core. See 'core'.

Reactor Pressure Vessel. The vessel containing the fuel assemblies, moderator and coolant of a reactor. Its purpose is to enable the reactor to be operated at pressures above atmospheric. In the case of the PWR it is made of steel.

Reactor Protection System. See 'protection system'.

Real Effective Exchange Rate. A real exchange rate measuring the movement of a given currency in terms of its purchasing power against a basket of other currencies.

Real Exchange Rate. The rate used to give a measure of the underlying change in the relative values of two currencies after removing the effects of inflation in the two countries. It is expressed as, for example:

$$\text{Change in nominal £ sterling: US dollar rate} \quad x \quad \frac{\text{Change in UK price level}}{\text{Change in US price level}}$$

Redundancy. The provision of more than the minimum amount of similar equipment than that necessary for performance of a given action thereby allowing the action to be performed when equipment is unavailable due to failure or maintenance.

Refill. The period in a large LOCA following blowdown (qv), during which the lower plenum fills with water. Refill finishes when the water level starts to move up the core.

Reflood. That period in a large LOCA during which the water level moves up the core. Reflood follows refill (qv).

Refuelling Water Storage Tank (RWST). A large tank of borated water in the auxiliary building. As well as allowing refuelling to be done under water, the RWST provides the initial source of water for the high and low head safety injection systems (qv).

Reliability. A measure of the probability that a system or component will work when required.

Reprocessing. The chemical treatment of spent fuel to separate the contained uranium, plutonium and fission products.

Residual Heat. Rate of generation of heat (usually in nuclear fuel) following shutdown, and due primarily to radioactive decay. Alternatively, the quantity of heat stored in a component or structure above a datum temperature.

Residual Heat Removal System (RHRS). The system which removes heat from the reactor coolant circuit at coolant temperatures below 177°C. The RHRS draws reactor coolant from two of the hot legs, and passes it through a set of heat exchangers in the auxiliary building.

Restricted Demand. The maximum demand on the CEGB system when consumers under load management arrangements have been asked to reduce load in accordance with the terms governing those arrangements.

Revealed Preference. The evaluation of public attitudes to risk by studying how the public actually behaves towards risk in practice.

Risk. See 'individual risk' and 'social risk'.

Risk Assessment. The study of decisions subject to uncertain consequences. Risk assessment comprises risk estimation (qv) and risk evaluation (qv).

Risk Estimation. That part of risk assessment which comprises
a) the identification of the outcomes;
b) the estimation of the magnitude of the consequences of these outcomes; and
c) the estimation of the probabilities of these outcomes.

Risk Evaluation. The process of determining the significance or value of the estimated risks to those people concerned with or affected by a decision.

Risk Factor. The probability of a stochastic (qv) effect occurring per unit dose equivalent, at low doses and dose rates.

Risk Weighting Factor. See 'weighting factor'.

Rod Cluster Control Assembly (RCCA). A linked assembly of 24 control rods; there would be 53 RCCAs in the Sizewell B reactor core.

Safety Relief Valve. A valve which opens automatically at a certain pressure to allow the escape to atmosphere of steam or other contents of a pressure vessel, so preventing a dangerous build-up of pressure.

Scenario. A possible picture of the future built up from a set of assumptions about the outcome of variable factors such as economic activity, energy supply and demand, and fuel prices.

Secondary Containment. An enclosure surrounding the primary containment which provides for the collection of leakage from the primary containment and filtering of the leakage before discharge to the atmosphere.

Segregation. The separation of components, whether diverse or redundant, by barriers to prevent all or most of the components being damaged in the event of a hazard.

Sensitivity Tests. Tests in which an uncertain parameter is varied over a range of plausible values to help determine the uncertainty in the results of an analysis.

Separate Effects Test. An experiment in which a particular phenomenon, such as the flow of steam and water through a nozzle, is isolated and examined.

Separation. In nuclear power station design, the separation of components, whether diverse or redundant, by distance to prevent all or most of the components being damaged in the event of a hazard.

Shut Down. The procedure of making a reactor subcritical.

Shutdown. Of a reactor, the state in which it is subcritical so that the chain reaction cannot be sustained.

Sievert. The special name for the SI unit of dose equivalent (qv).

Single Failure Criterion. A requirement placed on the designer to assume failure of at least one of the safety systems intended to prevent a particular initiating fault from leading to a degraded core.

Social Risk. A simple expression of social risk would be the expected average number of instances of a specified type or types of harm per unit time. For example, a social risk might be an expected average number of deaths per year. A full expression would state the probabilities of different numbers of instances of a specified type or types of harm per unit time.

Somatic Effects. Effects that arise from damage to the cells of the body. The term 'somatic' is used to distinguish those tissues or cells that die when the whole body dies, from genetic material which may be passed on to future generations. Thus somatic effects can only arise in the person whose body cells have been damaged. In contrast, damage to a person's genetic cells produces effects in their offspring and possibly in subsequent generations, but has no effect on the irradiated person.

Source Term. The fraction of the total amount of a particular category of fission products present in the core which is released to the environment in an accident.

Spent Fuel. Nuclear fuel whose period of irradiation in a reactor is complete.

Spent Fuel Flask. A large, heavily shielded container used for transporting spent fuel.

Stable Crack Growth. A mode of crack extension in which the resistance of the material to crack extension increases as the crack extends. As a result the crack extends in a slow and stable manner until it reaches a point of equilibrium when the force driving it is balanced by the increased resistance; crack growth then stops.

Standard Deviation. A measure of the spread of a set of values around their arithmetic average. It is calculated as the square root of the arithmetic average of the squares of the difference of each value from the arithmetic average.

Standardised Nuclear Unit Power Plant System. A nuclear power station design produced by five US utilities, based on a 1,150 MW(e) station design by Bechtel incorporating a 3,425 MW(t) four loop nuclear steam supply system by Westinghouse.

Start to Finish Allowance (SFA). A percentage added to the estimates of construction cost to allow for uncertainties in those estimtes.

Station Operating Instructions. Detailed procedures for operating the plant in normal and fault conditions.

Statistical Significance. A test of whether an observed set of data is consistent with the hypothesis that the data were generated in conformance with a specified statistical distribution.

Steam and Feed Valve Cell. A cell just outside the containment through which the main steam lines pass. Within the cell, each main steam line is connected to one power-operated relief valve and five safety relief valves. The cell also contains the main steam isolating valves (qv).

Steam Circuit. The circuit in which steam is produced in the steam generators, fed through turbine-generators, condensed and pumped back to the steam generators.

Steam Explosion. The explosive vaporisation of water when a sufficiently hot liquid is poured into it.

Steam Generator. A heat exchanger (qv) in which heat is transferred from the reactor coolant circuit to boiling water in the steam power plant.

Steam Power Plant. The steam circuit (qv), turbine-generators (qv) and associated plant.

Steam Spike. The rapid but non-explosive generation of steam.

Stochastic. When used in relation to the effects of radiation, it describes effects such as cancer and hereditary disease which do not get more severe as the dose increases but whose probability of occurrence increases as the dose increases.

Stress. The force acting upon a material and tending to change its dimensions. The intensity of stress or, more briefly, stress in the material is the force per unit area of the material resisting the force.

Substantial Issues. Those safety matters at issue between the CEGB and NII which might have added substantially to the time taken to grant a site licence, or to the cost of the station, or both. A 'substantial' increase in cost for Sizewell B was assumed by the NII to be of the order of £10 million.

Support Plates. Horizontal plates within the steam generator through which the steam generator tubes pass. The support plates hold the steam generator tubes in place.

Synchronisation. The time at which a new generating plant is first connected to the transmission system.

Systems Interactions. A plant failure which results from an interaction between plant systems; for example the failure of one component as the result of a missile (qv) created by the failure of another.

Tailings. Waste material (solid and liquid) produced as the result of the milling of uranium.

TAPSWEL. A computer code used in fuel clad ballooning (qv); TAPSWEL calculates the strain at which clad burst occurs.

Thermal Efficiency. A measure of the efficiency of converting fuel into electricity calculated by dividing equivalent heat units of the electrical output by heat supplied in the fuel used to produce that output. It is expressed as a percentage.

Thermal Neutrons. Neutrons in thermal equilibrium with the material in which they are moving, for example, in the moderator.

Thermal Reactor. A reactor in which the chain reaction is sustained by fission brought about primarily by thermal neutrons (qv). Such a reactor uses a moderator to slow down the neutrons produced in fission.

Thermal Stresses. Stresses which are set up as a result of heating or cooling or temperature change.

Thermohydraulic Analysis. The analysis of the temperature, pressure and motion of fluids.

Thirty Minute Rule. The requirement that designers must assume that no operator action is taken during the first thirty minutes of any accident.

Transformation, Radioactive. The spontaneous transformation from one radionuclide (qv) into another nuclide, which may or may not be stable, with the emission of radiation.

Transition Boiling. A mixture of film boiling (qv) and nucleate boiling (qv).

Transition Temperature. Steel is brittle below a certain temperature and ductile above. The temperature at which the transition occurs rises slowly with irradiation damage. Pressure vessels are normally operated well above the transition temperature so that there is no likelihood of brittle fracture.

Transmission System. The system the CEGB uses to supply electricity to the Area Boards. It is also known as the 'grid'. (That part of the system which connects the CEGB's power stations to the major demand centres at high voltage (mainly 400 kV) is known as the 'supergrid'). It is a network of cables and overhead lines, associated substations and control centres. Transmission plant which comprises transformers, switchgear, cables and overhead lines is connected to form a complete system with facilities for control, protection against faults of maloperation and communications.

Trip. Of a reactor, its rapid shutdown which is initiated when some operational parameter reaches a level determined by operational or safety requirements. In the PWR, tripping is achieved by dropping the control rods into the core.

Tubeplate. Fixing and supporting plate for the ends of steam generator tubes.

Turbine-Generator. An electric generator driven by a steam turbine.

Two-phase flow. The motion of a mixture of liquid and vapour through a system of pipes and vessels.

Ultrasonic Inspection. A method of detecting and sizing cracks or defects by injecting pulses of high-frequency sound into the material at different angles and measuring the reflected pulses.

Undermoderation. The provision of less that the optimum amount of moderator to maximise reactivity. If bubbles were to form in the core of an undermoderated reactor, for example as a result of increased reactor power or reduced system pressure, the amount of moderator in the core would decrease, and the reactor power would fall.

Unit Requirements. The total number of kWh to be supplied by the CEGB to the Area Boards and its direct consumers. The supplies include purchases by the CEGB from outside sources (less exports to SSEB and EdF).

Unrestricted Demand. The maximum demand on the CEGB system in the absence of the operation of any load management.

Upper Head. The hemispherical dome at the top of the reactor pressure vessel.

Upper Plenum. The region in the top of the reactor pressure vessel, above the core.

Validation. Of computer codes, the process of demonstrating that the results of a particular code are an adequate representation of the physical processes involved.

Water Hammer. A phenomenon which occurs when steam condenses rapidly; a high velocity flow of water is produced which may exert considerable force on reactor coolant circuit pipework.

Weighting Factor. The risk arising from irradiation of an organ or tissue as a fraction of the risk arising from uniform irradiation of the whole body to the same dose equivalent. If an organ with a weighting factor W is irradiated to a dose equivalent of H, the effective dose equivalent (qv) is WH.

Zircaloy. The zirconium alloy used for canning fuel in water reactors because it has acceptable physical properties and in particular is relatively non-absorbent of thermal neutrons.

INDEX

INDEX

INDEX

AGR SAFETY
                    88.9-10
AGRICULTURE
        EFFECTS OF BEYOND DESIGN BASIS ACCIDENTS ON, 33.67-70
AIRCRAFT CRASH
        AS HAZARDS, 26.16-23
ALARA PRINCIPLE
        IN RADIOLOGICAL PROTECTION, 7.13
ALARP PRINCIPLE
        APPLICATION OF, AND COST-BENEFIT ANALYSIS IN NUCLEAR
                LICENSING, 49.48-53
                TO NUCLEAR SAFETY, 35.41-43
                        35.8-26, 50.39-43, 7.41-53
                TO REFERENCE DESIGN 1981 AND REFERENCE DESIGN 1982
                        37.20-23
                TO REPLICATED SIZEWELL B DESIGN, 51.8-11
                TO RISK ASSESSMENT, 12.31-33
        IN RADIOLOGICAL PROTECTION, 7.13
AMBULANCE SERVICES
        EFFECT OF SIZEWELL B ON, 101.51
AONB
        DESIGNATION OF, AND SUFFOLK HERITAGE COAST, 95.6-8
APPENDIX K CRITERIA
        FOR LOCA ANALYSIS, 23.21-24
ARCHITECTURE
        OF SIZEWELL B, 100.15-22
                        100.41-45
                UNDERTAKINGS ON, 100.19
AREA OF OUTSTANDING NATURAL BEAUTY
        SEE AONB
AS LOW AS REASONABLY ACHIEVABLE
        SEE ALARA PRINCIPLE
AS LOW AS REASONABLY PRACTICABLE
        SEE ALARP PRINCIPLE
ATKINS REPORT
        ON CHP/DH, 58.6
ATMOSPHERIC FLUIDISED BED COMBUSTION
                    60.9
ATOMIC BOMB SURVIVORS
        ESTIMATES OF RADIATION DOSE TO, 30.37-39
ATOMIC ENERGY AUTHORITY
        SEE UKAEA
AUSTRALIA
        URANIUM MINING IN, 106.38-43
AUTHORISING DEPARTMENTS
        SEE ALSO DEPT OF ENVIRONMENT, MAFF
        ROLE OF, IN NUCLEAR REGULATION, 50.13-22
AUXILIARY FEEDWATER SYSTEM
        SEE AFWS
AUXILIARY SHUT-DOWN ROOM
        FUNCTION OF, 15.47

INDEX

CEGB

CONSTRUCTION PERFORMANCE OF, IN POWER STATIONS
CONSTRUCTION, 66.5-26
IN POWER STATIONS CONSTRUCTION, 69.2-16
FINANCIAL CONTRIBUTIONS BY, TO EDUCATION SERVICES, 102.11
TO IMPROVEMENTS TO ROAD SYSTEM, 102.9-10
TO SWIMMING POOL IN LEISTON, 102.12-13
MANAGEMENT OF NUCLEAR LICENSING BY, AND NII, 49.1-92
RELATIONSHIP BETWEEN, AND LOCAL COMMUNITY, 103.1-24
AND NII FOR NUCLEAR LICENSING, 49.11-43
9.25-29
RISK ASSESSMENT OF SIZEWELL B BY, 12.42-52
STATUTORY DUTY OF, UNDER ELECTRICITY ACT 1947, 107.49-51
UNDER ELECTRICITY ACT 1957, 107.25-31
107.43-48
UNDER NUCLEAR INSTALLATIONS ACT 1965, 107.7-24
FOR NUCLEAR SAFETY, 4.8

CEGB DESIGN SAFETY CRITERIA
SEE DESIGN SAFETY CRITERIA
CEGB DESIGN SAFETY GUIDELINES
SEE DESIGN SAFETY GUIDELINES
CEGB HEALTH AND SAFETY DEPT
SEE HSD
CENTRAL ELECTRICITY GENERATING BOARD
SEE CEGB
CERG COMPUTER MODEL
CALCULATIONS OF NEC BY, 78.7-11
CHEMICAL AND VOLUME CONTROL SYSTEM
FUNCTION OF, 15.30-33
CHP
INDUSTRIAL
EFFECT OF ENERGY ACT 1983 ON, 85.18-19
FINANCIAL VIABILITY OF, 85.20-24
INFLUENCE OF, ON CAPACITY NEED, 85.5-34
POTENTIAL CONTRIBUTION OF, TO GENERATING CAPACITY,
85.25-28
CHP/DH
ALLOWANCES FOR, IN PLANNING BACKGROUNDS, 58.10-11
AS ALTERNATIVE TO SIZEWELL B, 58.9-49
TO SIZEWELL B, 63.6
ATKINS REPORT ON, 58.6
ECONOMIC COMPARISON OF, AND SIZEWELL B, 58.23-37
MARSHALL REPORT ON, 58.5
POTENTIAL DEVELOPMENT OF, IN UK, 58.38-44
PROPOSALS BY GLC FOR, IN LONDON, 58.13-14
GLC FOR, IN LONDON, 58.18-22
PROVISIONS FOR, IN ENERGY ACT 1983, 58.2
CO-PROCESSING
OF PLUTONIUM AT SELLAFIELD, 105.36-40
COAL FIRED POWER STATIONS
SEE ALSO OIL TO COAL CONVERSION
AS ALTERNATIVE TO SIZEWELL B, 57.7-10

INDEX

INDEX

INDEX

INTERNATIONAL ATOMIC ENERGY AGENCY
        SEE IAEA
INTERNATIONAL COMMISSION ON RADIOLOGICAL PROTECTION
        SEE ICRP
IRR
        USE OF, IN COMPARATIVE INVESTMENT APPRAISALS, 55.42-45
IRRADIATED FUEL
        SEE SPENT FUEL

MAFF
> SEE ALSO AUTHORISING DEPARTMENTS
> ROLE OF DEPT OF ENVIRONMENT AND, IN RADIOACTIVE WASTE
> > MANAGEMENT, 7.29-31

MAGNETOHYDRODYNAMIC GENERATION
> 60.13

MAGNOX REACTORS
> CAPITAL COSTS OF, 66.7
> CONSTRUCTION TIMES OF, 66.10
> PROGRAMME OF, 3.2-7

MAIN CONTROL ROOM
> FUNCTION OF, 15.45
> INFLUENCE OF HUMAN FACTORS ON, 25.17-23
> MANNING OF, 25.39-43

MAIN FEEDWATER LOSS
> ACCIDENT PROBABILITY ANALYSIS OF, 28.45-46

MAIN STEAM LINE BREAK
> REACTOR PRESSURE VESSEL INTEGRITY AFTER, 21.47

MAINTENANCE
> OPERATOR ERROR IN, 25.75-82

MARSHALL REPORT
> ON CHP/DH, 58.5
> ON REACTOR PRESSURE VESSEL INTEGRITY, 3.36-37
> > 6.7

> ON REACTOR PRESSURE VESSEL INTEGRITY, 21.16,19

MEDIUM NUCLEAR BACKGROUND
> SEE PLANT BACKGROUNDS

MERIT ORDER
> OF GENERATING CAPACITY, 53.19-27

MINISTRY OF AGRICULTURE FISHERIES AND FOOD
> SEE MAFF

MORTALITY STUDY
> OF RADIATION WORKERS AT SELLAFIELD, 30.42-45

MUTUAL DEFENCE AGREEMENT 1958
> EXPORTS OF PLUTONIUM TO USA UNDER, 105.20-35

NAC
        SEE ALSO COST-SAVING CASE, NEC
        CALCULATIONS OF, IN COST-SAVING CASE, 55.38-39
NAMIBIA
        URANIUM MINING IN, 106.44-51
NATIONAL INCOME
        EFFECT OF SIZEWELL B ON, AND EMPLOYMENT, 89.10-55
                SIZEWELL B ON, AND EMPLOYMENT, 90.19
NATIONAL NEED
        FOR SIZEWELL B, 104.10-11
                95.18-21
NATIONAL NUCLEAR CORPORATION
        SEE NNC
NATIONAL RADIOLOGICAL PROTECTION BOARD
        SEE NRPB
NEC
        SEE ALSO COST-SAVING CASE, NAC
        OF AGR, 88.4-5
        CALCULATIONS OF, BY CERG COMPUTER MODEL, 78.7-11
                BY COMPUTER MODELS, 78.3-11
                CONVERSION OF WORLD COAL PRICES FOR, 73.34-40
                IN COST-SAVING CASE, 55.29-37
                        65.1-8
                DECOMMISSIONING COSTS IN, 75.35-39
                IMPORTANCE OF FOSSIL FUEL PRICES IN, 70.1-6
                NUCLEAR FUEL CYCLE COSTS IN, 75.4-20
                OPERATING COSTS IN, 75.25-34
                PLANT PERFORMANCE IN, 74.1-120
                UNCERTAINTIES IN, 78.13-26
        EFFECT OF ELECTRICITY DEMAND ON, 76.10-12
                OIL TO COAL CONVERSION ON, 77.40-43
                PLANNING BACKGROUNDS ON, 77.1-4
                        77.23-49
                PLANNING MARGIN ON, 77.38-39
                PLANT LIFETIME IN PLANNING BACKGROUNDS ON, 77.44
        FINAL CALCULATIONS ON AVAILABILITY IN, 79.40
                CAPITAL COSTS IN, 79.33-37
                CONSTRUCTION TIMES IN, 79.38-39
                ELECTRICITY DEMAND IN, 79.51
                FOSSIL FUEL PRICES IN, 79.44-47
                LIFETIME IN, 79.42-43
                NUCLEAR FUEL CYCLE COSTS IN, 79.48-49
                OPERATING COSTS IN, 79.50
                PLANT PERFORMANCE IN, 79.40-43
                RATING IN, 79.41
                FOR SIZEWELL B AND AGR AND COAL FIRED POWER
                    STATIONS, ANNEX 78.1
                        79.31-61
        INFLUENCE OF OIL PRICES ON, 72.1-3
        RELATIONSHIP BETWEEN, AND DEFERMENT COST IN COST-SAVING
                    CASE, ANNEX 77.3

NII

(CONTINUED)
ON OCCUPATIONAL RADIATION EXPOSURE, 31.58-63
ON QUALITY ASSURANCE, 20.23-26
ON REACTOR PRESSURE VESSEL INTEGRITY, 21.146-147
NII OPERATORS IN NUCLEAR SAFETY WORKING GROUP
SEE ONSWG
NII SAFETY ASSESSMENT PRINCIPLES
SEE SAFETY ASSESSMENT PRINCIPLES
NIREX
ROLE OF, IN RADIOACTIVE WASTE MANAGEMENT, 7.34-35
NNC
ROLE OF, IN PROJECT MANAGEMENT, 68.21
THERMAL REACTOR ASSESSMENT BY, 3.25-27
6.7
NO NEW NUCLEAR BACKGROUND
SEE PLANT BACKGROUNDS
NOISE
ENVIRONMENTAL EFFECTS OF, 99.32-35
99.36
CONDITIONS ON, ANNEX 99.1
NRPB
ROLE OF, IN NUCLEAR REGULATION, 50.28-31
IN RADIOLOGICAL PROTECTION, 30.53-54
7.3-8
NSSS
WESTINGHOUSE AS LICENSOR FOR, 6.14-16
NUCLEAR ACCIDENTS
DESIGN SAFETY CRITERIA FOR, 13.38-47
ENGINEERING CRITERIA FOR, 13.36-37
ERLS OF RADIATION DOSE FOR COUNTERMEASURES IN, 13.32-33
INCIDENT REPORTING OF, 46.11-14
RECOMMENDATIONS OF ICRP ON COUNTERMEASURES IN, 13.29-30
RISKS OF CANCER FROM SAFETY ASSESSMENT PRINCIPLES FOR,
13.54-55
SAFETY ASSESSMENT PRINCIPLES FOR, 13.48-51
NUCLEAR EXPLOSION
IN PWR, 5.44-47
NUCLEAR FUEL
URANIUM AS, 5.12-14
NUCLEAR FUEL CYCLE
DESCRIPTION OF, 38.6-21
SAFETY IN, 38.22-32
NUCLEAR FUEL CYCLE COSTS
IN CALCULATIONS OF NEC, 75.4-20
ESTIMATES OF, FOR AGR, 75.21-24
FOR SIZEWELL B, 75.4-20
75.40-44
FINAL CALCULATIONS ON, IN NEC, 79.48-49
SENSITIVITY TESTS ON, IN NEC, 79.20
NUCLEAR FUSION
POTENTIAL OF, FOR ELECTRICITY GENERATION, 60.21-22

NUCLEAR SAFETY

INDEX

RADIATION DOSE
        SEE ALSO RADIATION EXPOSURE
        CONTROL OF, FROM RADIOACTIVE WASTE, 32.7-9
        FROM DESIGN BASIS ACCIDENTS, 33.24-38
        ERLS OF, FOR COUNTERMEASURES IN NUCLEAR ACCIDENTS,
                13.32-33
        ESTIMATES OF, TO ATOMIC BOMB SURVIVORS, 30.37-39
                TO PUBLIC FROM SIZEWELL A AND SIZEWELL B, 32.5-45
                FROM SIZEWELL B ACCIDENTS, 33.15-16
        MEASUREMENT OF, 11.22-28
        RECOMMENDATIONS OF ICRP ON, FOR OCCUPATIONAL RADIATION
                EXPOSURE, 13.7-15
                ICRP ON, TO PUBLIC, 13.19-23
                        30.55-57
        SOURCES OF, IN REACTOR COOLANT CIRCUIT, 31.21-25
    LOW LEVEL
        HEALTH EFFECTS OF, 30.40-45
RADIATION EXPOSURE
        SEE ALSO RADIATION DOSE

        CRITERIA FOR, FROM RADIOACTIVE WASTE, 13.25-28
        CRITICISMS OF ICRP RISK FACTORS FOR CANCER FROM, 30.10-36
        HEALTH EFFECTS TO EMBRYO AND FOETUS FROM, 11.73-76
        HEALTH EFFECTS OF, 11.29-76
        ICRP RISK FACTORS FOR CANCER FROM, 30.6-9
        OF PUBLIC FROM REPROCESSING AT SELLAFIELD, 40.20-26
        RISKS OF CANCER FROM, 11.47-65
                HEREDITARY DISEASE FROM, 11.67-69
        SOURCES OF, 11.13-21
    OCCUPATIONAL
        CEGB ESTIMATES OF, AT SIZEWELL B, 31.35-47
        CEGB RECORD ON, 31.17-19
        CONCLUSIONS ON, 47.47
        CONTROL OF, IN SIZEWELL B DESIGN, 31.27-34
        CRITERIA FOR, 31.11-16
        DESIGN SAFETY CRITERIA FOR, 13.16,18
        ESTIMATES OF, FROM REFERENCE DESIGN 1981 AND REFERENCE
                DESIGN 1982, 37.18-19
        MONITORING OF, 31.5-8
        RECOMMENDATIONS OF ICRP ON RADIATION DOSE FOR, 13.7-15
        FROM REPROCESSING AT SELLAFIELD, 40.5-19
        SAFETY ASSESSMENT PRINCIPLES FOR, 13.17
        FROM STEAM GENERATORS, 22.27
        VIEWS OF NII ON, 31.58-63
RADIATION WORKERS
        MORTALITY STUDY OF, AT SELLAFIELD, 30.42-45
RADIOACTIVE RELEASE CATEGORIES
        FROM DEGRADED CORE ACCIDENTS, TAB 29.1
RADIOACTIVE RELEASES
        FROM DESIGN BASIS ACCIDENTS, 27.20-25
        ESTIMATES OF, FROM SIZEWELL B ACCIDENTS, 33.9-14

INDEX

INDEX

INDEX

APPENDICES

A   Key Events Table

B   List of Meetings Not Forming Part of the Inquiry

C   List of Site Inspections

D   Correspondence Between the Inspector and the Secretary of State for Energy About the Funding of Objectors

E   Members of the Secretariat and Counsel to the Inquiry

F   List of Appearances

G   Letters of Objection and Written Representations

H   Alphabetical List of Statements of Case, Proofs of Evidence and Addenda

I   List of Documents Introduced by Counsel to the Inquiry

KEY EVENTS TABLE

This table is based largely on document CI/86
which was drawn up during the Inquiry to assist
cross-examination. Parties were asked to
notify the Inquiry of any inaccuracies.
Comments received have been taken into account and
a number of additions have been made.

DATE	SOURCE	EVENT	EVENT BY				COMMENT
			Govt	CEGB	BNFL	NNC	Other	
1948	CEGB/S/34	Radioactive Substances Act 1948	*					
1954	CEGB/S/33	Atomic Energy Authority Act 1954 which established the UKAEA	*					
1955 February	Day 7 page 64F-G CEGB/S/22	"A Programme of Nuclear Power" (Cmd 9389)	*					UK's first nuclear power programme: 1500-2000 MW nuclear capacity by 1965
1956	CEGB 01 para 5.8	1st Calder Hall reactor commissioned						Provided design basis for Magnox stations
1957 March	CEGB/S/23 para 2	Announced in Parliament that nuclear programme being trebled to 5000-6000 MW of nuclear power by 1965	*					
1957 25 March	CEGB 01 para 12.21	European Atomic Energy Community (EURATOM) set up					*	
1957 October	NRPB/S/2	Windscale reactor fire						
1957	CEGB 01 table 6.1	Bradwell (Magnox) station ordered		*				1st Magnox station ordered (commissioned in 1962)
1957	CEGB 01 table 6.1	Berkeley (Magnox) station ordered		*				2nd Magnox station ordered (commissioned in 1962)
1957	CEGB 01 table 6.1	Hinkley Point A (Magnox) station ordered		*				3rd Magnox station ordered (commissioned in 1965)

2

DATE	SOURCE	EVENT	EVENT BY					COMMENT
			Govt	CEGB	BNFL	NNC	Other	
1957	CEGB/S/20	Electricity Act 1957	*					
1957	CEGB 01 para 12.20	IAEA set up					*	
1958	CEGB/P/25 (Add 4) table 1 page 10	Adoption of Sizewell site by CEGB (for more than 1 station)		*				
1959 November	CEGB 01 para 27.6 CEGB/S/79	"The Control of Radioactive Wastes" (Cmnd 884)	*					
1959	CEGB/P/25 (Add 4) table 1 page 10	Section 2 application for Sizewell A station		*				
1959	CEGB 01 table 6.1	Trawsfynydd (Magnox) station ordered		*				4th Magnox station ordered (commissioned in 1965)
1959	CEGB 01 para 12.14	Nuclear Installations (Licensing and Insurance) Act 1959	*					
1960 April	Day 56 page 48F-G	NII established	*					
1960 June	CEGB/S/23 para 2	"The nuclear power programme" (Cmnd 1083)	*					Period for the nuclear power programme, announced in 1957(qv), extended to 1968 for 5000 MW

3

DATE	SOURCE	EVENT	EVENT BY				COMMENT
			Govt	CEGB	BNFL	NNC	Other	
1960	CEGB 01 table 6.1	Dungeness A (Magnox) station ordered		*				5th Magnox station ordered (commissioned in 1965)
1960	CEGB 01 table 6.1	Sizewell A (Magnox) station ordered		*				6th Magnox station ordered (commissioned in 1966)
1960	CEGB 01 para 12.14 CEGB/S/36	Radioactive Substances Act 1960	*					Controls keeping, using, of radioactive material, and accumulation and disposal of radioactive waste
1960	Day 47 page 62G-63A	Radiochemical Inspectorate established	*					Part of DOE
1962	CEGB 01 table 6.1	Oldbury (Magnox) station ordered		*				7th Magnox station ordered (commissioned in 1967)
1962	CEGB 01 table 6.1	Bradwell (Magnox) station commissioned		*				1st Magnox station commissioned
1962	CEGB 01 table 6.1	Berkeley (Magnox) station commissioned		*				2nd Magnox station commissioned
1963 1 December	CEGB 01 para 27.6	Guidelines (set out in Cmnd 884) in Radio-active Substances Act 1960 on control of radioactive waste came into effect	*					
1963	CEGB 01 table 6.1	Wylfa (Magnox) station ordered		*				8th Magnox station (commissioned in 1971)

4

DATE	SOURCE	EVENT	EVENT BY					COMMENT
			Govt	CEGB	BNFL	NNC	Other	
1964	Day 7 page 66D CEGB/S/23 para 11	"The Second Nuclear Power Programme" (Cmnd 2335)	*					5 GW of nuclear plant 1970-75
1965	CEGB 01 table 6.1	Hinkley Point A (Magnox) station commissioned		*				3rd Magnox station commissioned
1965	CEGB 01 table 6.1	Trawsfynydd (Magnox) station commissioned		*				4th Magnox station commissioned
1965	CEGB 01 table 6.1	Dungeness A (Magnox) station commissioned		*				5th Magnox station commissioned
1965	CEGB 01 table 6.2	Dungeness B (AGR) station ordered	*	*				1st AGR station to be ordered
1965	CEGB/S/18	Nuclear Installations Act 1965						
1966	CEGB 01 table 6.1	Sizewell A (Magnox) station commissioned		*				6th Magnox station commissioned
1967	CEGB 01 table 6.1	Oldbury (Magnox) station commissioned		*				7th Magnox station commissioned
1967	CEGB 01 table 6.2	Hinkley Point B (AGR) station ordered		*				2nd AGR station to be ordered (commissioned in 1976)

5

DATE	SOURCE	EVENT	Govt	CEGB	BNFL	NNC	Other	COMMENT
1968	CEGB/P/25 (Add 4) table 1 page 10	Section 2 application for Sizewell B site (2500 MW AGR)		*				
1968	CEGB 01 table 6.2	Hartlepool (AGR) station ordered		*				3rd AGR station to be ordered
1969	CEGB/P/25 (Add 4) table 1 page 10	Consent given for Sizewell B station (2500 MW AGR)	*					
1969	Day 15 page 21F-G CEGB/S/120	Report of Wilson Committee of Inquiry into delays in commissioning of CEGB power stations (Cmnd 3960)	*					Particularly on construction delays
1969	CEGB 01 para 12.2 CEGB/S/38	Nuclear Installations Act 1969	*					
1969	CEGB/P/25 (Add 4) table 1 page 10	Designation of Suffolk Coast and Heaths Area of Outstanding Natural Beauty	*					Sizewell site is within AONB
1970	CEGB/P/25 (Add 4) table 1 page 10	Confirmation of Suffolk Coast and Heaths Area of Outstanding Natural Beauty	*					Sizewell site is within AONB

DATE	SOURCE	EVENT	EVENT BY					COMMENT
			Govt	CEGB	BNFL	NNC	Other	
1970 May	Day 15 page 30E-F CEGB/S/397	NEDO Report on large industrial construction sites					*	
1970	CEGB/P/25 (Add 4) table 1 page 10	Suffolk Heritage Coast Identified					*	Sizewell site is within Suffolk Heritage Coast
1970	CEGB 01 table 6.2	Heysham 1 (AGR) station ordered		*				4th AGR station to be ordered
1970	CEGB 01 para 12.15 CEGB/S/39	The Radiological Protection Act 1970	*					Set up NRPB
1970	DTp/P/1 (App 2)	The Radioactive Substances (Road Transport Workers) (Great Britain) Regulations 1970	*					(SI 1970 No.1827)
1971	Day 191 page 3F CI/80 page 233	Results published by US Pressure Vessel Research Council on effectiveness of manual ultrasonic tests					*	Showed that manual ultrasonic tests applied by experienced operators working to American Society of Mechanical Engineers (ASME) XI requirements found only about two thirds of the defects intentionally placed in a thick welded pressure vessel steel test block
1971	CEGB/P/25 (Add 4) table 1 page 10	Work stopped on Sizewell B AGR		*				Preliminary site work had been carried out. Work stopped due to delays to other AGRs then under construction and forecasts for reduced electricity demand (see CEGB 01 Chapter 1.2)

7

DATE	SOURCE	EVENT	EVENT BY					COMMENT
			Govt	CEGB	BNFL	NNC	Other	
1971	CEGB 01 table 6.1	Wylfa (Magnox) station commissioned		*				8th Magnox station commissioned
1972 8 August	Day 7 page 67B-C CEGB/S/132	Government statement on restructuring of nuclear design and construction industry and setting up of NPAB	*					Nuclear Power Advisory Board chaired by Secretary of State for Trade and Industry. Its purpose was "to provide continuing and concerted advice on all strategic aspects of civil nuclear energy policy"
1972	CEGB/S/45	European Communities Act 1972	*					
1972	QLC/S/123	Local Government Act 1972	*					
1973	CEGB 01 para 28.9	Revised edition of regulations by IAEA for the safe transportation of radioactive materials and design of flasks					*	This is the current edition
1973	CEGB/P/25 (Add 4) table 1 page 10	Suffolk Heritage Coast length defined					*	Identified 1970 (qv). Sizewell site is within Suffolk Heritage Coast
1973	Day 7 page 75B	SNUPPS project initiated					*	By a group of American utilities with objective of adopting a common station design
1973	CEGB/P/25 (Add 4) table 1 page 10	CEGB make alternative Section 2 application for Sizewell B Station 2500MW of SGHWR, or LWR or HTR		*				Earlier Section 2 application (AGR) in 1968 (qv)

8

DATE	SOURCE	EVENT	Govt	CEGB	BNFL	NNC	Other	COMMENT
1974 July	Day 7 page 68A CEGB/S/25	"Nuclear Reactor Systems for Electricity Generation". (Cmnd 5695)	*					SGHWR the next reactor system – "not more than 4000 MW over the next 4 years"
1974 September	CEGB 01 para 6.6 CEGB/S/24	"Choice of Thermal Reactor Systems" (Cmnd 5731)	*					Report of NPAB. Choice narrowed to PWR and SGHWR
1974	CI/31	The Nuclear Installations Act 1965 etc. (Repeals and Modifications) Regulations 1974	*					Established role of HSE in granting Nuclear Site Licences
1974	CEGB 01 para 12.18 CEGB/S/41	Health and Safety at Work etc. Act 1974	*					Set up HSC and HSE (of which NII forms part)
1974	DTp/P/1 (App 2)	The Radioactive Substances (Carriage by Road) (Great Britain) Regulations 1974	*					(SI 1974 No.1735)
1974	Day 55 page 60F-G MAFF/S/17	Dumping at Sea Act 1974	*					Controls disposal of solid radioactive waste at sea
1974	Day 8 page 57C-D	1st version of Design Safety Guidelines produced for SGHWR project		*				
1974	LPA/S/100	Control of Pollution Act 1974	*					
1974	Day 7 page 74B	NNC agreement with Westinghouse				*		Limited access to PWR design and safety information
1975	NNC/P/1 (App 2)	NNC Technical Assistance and Patent Licence Agreements with Westinghouse				*		

DATE	SOURCE	EVENT	EVENT BY					COMMENT
			Govt	CEGB	BNFL	NNC	Other	
1975	Day 55 page 62D-F	London Dumping Convention (Prevention of Marine Pollution by Dumping of Wastes and Other Matter (Cmnd 5169)) came into force	*					
1975	CEGB/P/25 (Add 4) table 1 page 10	Consent granted for Sizewell B Station (2500MW SGHWR)	*					
1975	DTp/P/1 (App 2)	The Radioactive Substances (Road Transport Workers) (Great Britain) Amendment Regulations 1975	*					Amends 1970 Regulations (qv) (SI 1975 No.1522)
1975	Day 316 page 28D	Publication of Rasmussen Report (WASH 1400)					*	Concerning Assessment of Accident Risks in US Commercial Nuclear Power Plants
1976	CEGB 01 table 6.2	Hinkley Point B (AGR) station commissioned		*				1st AGR station to be commissioned
1976 September	CEGB 01 para 14.43 CEGB/S/A7	Publication of Nuclear Power and the Environment. (6th Report of Royal Commission on Environmental Pollution) (Cmnd 6618)					*	Flowers Report
1976 October	CEGB 01 para 6.7	Secretary of State for Energy authorises NNC to undertake review of PWR, SGHWR and AGR	*					
1976 October	Day 191 page 4E CEGB/S/558	Publication of CEGB's R6 methodology for critical crack detection		*				Updated in April 1980

DATE	SOURCE	EVENT	EVENT BY					COMMENT
			Govt	CEGB	BNFL	NNC	Other	
1976 October	Day 7 page 68D CEGB/S/130	"An assessment of the integrity of PWR pressure vessels." Report by a Study Group chaired by Dr W Marshall (UKAEA)					*	Response to Sixth Report of RCEP (1976) (qv)
1977 May	CEGB 01 para 27.7 CEGB/S/80	"Nuclear Power and the Environment" (Cmnd 6820)	*					No fundamental reason to regard safety as obstacle to PWR
1977 July	NII 01 para 2.4 CEGB/S/127	Generic safety study of PWR system by NII; scope and main conclusions presented to Secretary of State for Energy						
1977 October	Day 7 page 68F CEGB/S/138	"Thermal Reactor Assessment". Final Report of Thermal Reactor Working Party		*				Formed basis, together with other studies, for CEGB's thermal reactor strategy
1977	CEGB 01 para 6.7 CEGB/S/58	NNC report of review of PWR, SGHWR and AGR "The choice of thermal reactor systems"				*		SGHWR should be discontinued. PWR and/or AGR should replace it
1977	Day 55 page 62D-E, 63E-F	Multilateral Consultation and Surveillance Mechanism for Sea Dumping of Radioactive Waste adopted	*					Mechanism established by OECD and managed by OECD's NEA
1977	CEGB/P/23 (App 3)	List of dangerous goods and conditions of acceptance by freight trains etc. (BR 22426) (1977 Edition)					*	This is current edition. Class 7 deals with radioactive materials. (Conditions made by BR under S.43 of Transport Act 1962)
1977	BNFL/S/2	Windscale Public Inquiry						

DATE	SOURCE	EVENT	Govt	CEGB	BNFL	NNC	Other	COMMENT
1978 25 January	CEGB 01 para 1.4	Statement on nuclear reactor policy	*					Discontinue SGHWR. Future programme to have option of AGR and PWR
1978 26 January	Day 56 page 14D-E	Windscale Inquiry Report presented to Secretary of State for the Environment					*	
1978 March	Day 7 page 54A-B CEGB/S/59	"The Nationalised Industries" (Cmnd 7131)	*					5% RRR recommended for assessing public sector capital expenditure
1978 April	Day 18 page 65E-F	CEGB place contract with NNC to develop the design of a PWR station		*				
1978 October	CEGB/P/25 (Add 2) page 2	Decision to select Sizewell as first PWR site		*				
1978 November	CEGB 01 para 30.13 CEGB/S/96	"Suffolk Heritage Coast Plan" issued by SCC					*	
1978	Day 55 page 2D-G MAFF/S/18	IAEA revise definition and recommendations concerning radioactive wastes and other radioactive matter					*	Original definition and recommendations in Annex I & II of 1975 London Dumping Convention (qv)
1978	CEGB/S/82 page 3	Radioactive Waste Management Advisory Committee (RWMAC) set up	*					
1979 March	CEGB/S/139	Three Mile Island accident					*	

DATE	SOURCE	EVENT	EVENT BY					COMMENT
			Govt	CEGB	BNFL	NNC	Other	
1979	CEGB/P/25 (Add 4) table 1 page 10	Suffolk Heritage Coast Area defined					*	Identified 1970 (qv) and coast length 1973 (qv) Sizewell site is within Suffolk Heritage Coast
1979 April	CEGB 01 para 14.68 CEGB/S/57	Publication of "Safety assessment principles for nuclear power reactors" by NII					*	
1979 June	Day 18 page 57B Day 7 page 74F Day 8 page 18A-B	CEGB confirm choice of NSSS design and Westinghouse as licensor		*				
1979 September	CEGB 01 para 30.13 CEGB/S/91	Suffolk C.C. Structure Plan approved by Secretary of State for the Environment	*					

DATE	SOURCE	EVENT	Govt	CEGB	BNFL	NNC	Other	COMMENT
			EVENT BY					
1979 September	Day 47 page 48G-49B CEGB/S/81	"A Review of Cmnd 884: 'The Control of Radioactive Wastes'". (Report of an expert group published by DOE)	*					Cmnd 884 (1959) (qv)
1979 November	FOE "Bundle D"	Draft Annexes to PWR Design Safety requirements and criteria		*				Draft annexes on reliability requirements for trip, shutdown and other essential systems; specification for reactor safety systems; radiological limits for accidental release of radioactivity to the atmosphere
1979	CEGB 01 para 30.13 CEGB/S/94	"Leiston Issues Report" by SCDC					*	
1979	CEGB 01 para 30.13 CEGB/S/95	"Saxmundham and Kelsale Issues Report and By-Pass Options" by SCC and SCDC					*	
1979 April	Day 56 page 2C CEGB/S/304	OECD publishes revised version of Guidelines for sea dumping packages of radioactive waste					*	
1979	Day 191 page 4F	Results of PISC (Plant Inspection Steering Committee) I trials (based on ASME section 3) published					*	
1979 18 December	CEGB 01 para 1.5 CEGB/S/6	Government statement on nuclear policy	*					Endorsed January 1978 statement (qv): one nuclear station a year in decade from 1982

14

DATE	SOURCE	EVENT	EVENT BY Govt	CEGB	BNFL	NNC	Other	COMMENT
1980 30 January	CEGB/S/26A	1st appearance of Secretary of State for Energy (Mr Howell) before Select Committee on Energy on Government's statement on the new nuclear power programme	*					
1980 13 February	NII/P/2 (Add 19) page 11-27 Day 320 page 110A	Series of meetings, correspondence and submissions began between NII and CEGB on licensing Sizewell B	*	*			*	
1980 26 March	CEGB/S/26B page 188-222	HSE evidence (Mr Dunster) before Select Committee on Energy	*					(1) NII not received any detailed design for PWR (2) Anticipates virtual licence for PWR by Inquiry in 1982 (3) Requires 2 years from application to achieve (2)
1980 2 April	Day 315 page 8C CEGB/S/60	CEGB issues Enquiry Specification to NNC		*				
1980 18 April	CEGB 01 para 1.6 CEGB/S/7	CEGB issue letter of intent to NNC		*				Authorised design and, subject to approval, manufacture of PWR. (This activated 1975 Technical Assistance and Patent Licence agreements (qv) between NNC and Westinghouse)
1980 April	NNC/P/1 (App 2) page 92	NNC - Westinghouse Technical Assistance and Patent Licence Agreement activitated				*		Following 18 April 1980 CEGB letter of Intent (qv)

DATE	SOURCE	EVENT	EVENT BY					COMMENT
			Govt	CEGB	BNFL	NNC	Other	
1980 April	CEGB 01 para 6.22	BNFL - Westinghouse PWR fuel licence agreement activated			*			
1980 April	Day 191 page 4E CEGB/S/558	CEGB's R6 methodology for critical crack detection revised		*				Originally published in October 1976 (qv)
1980 June	NII 01 para 2.5	NII requirements for programme of CEGB safety submissions leading to licensing agreed	*					Programme similar to that for new AGRs, but increased emphasis on design description and fault analysis. Main elements of programme agreed subsequently:- mid-July '80: Westinghouse SNUPPS Final Safety Analysis Report and commentary on it; end-Sept '80: Preliminary Safety Report for proposed UK design; mid-Feb '81: major part of safety case and full set of representative fault studies together with draft PCSR; mid-Nov '81: completion of draft PCSR; mid-Feb '82: publication of final draft PCSR. NII to begin preparation of draft report; May '82: publication of NII report
1980 19 June	NNC/P/1 (App 2) page 93	NNC Agreement with Bechtel				*		Gave access to certain PWR generic documentation and made available to NNC Bechtel experience of PWR projects

DATE	SOURCE	EVENT	EVENT BY					COMMENT
			Govt	CEGB	BNFL	NNC	Other	
1980 July	NII 01 para 2.5(a) and 2.7	CEGB submit Westinghouse SNUPPS Final Safety Analysis Report to NII		*				
1980 30 July	CEGB/S/26A	2nd appearance of Secretary of State for Energy (Mr Howell) before Select Committee on Energy on Government's statement on the new nuclear power programme	*					
1980 August	NNC 01 para 6.3 (ref 15)	NNC enters into Consulting Services Agreement with Westinghouse					*	
1980 August	CEGB/P/8B Diagram 2	Heysham II : start main foundations		*				
1980 September	Day 55 page 77F MAFF/S/20	EEC Directive on Radiation Protection					*	
1980 1 October	CEGB 01 para 1.6	CEGB announce publicly proposals to construct first PWR at Sizewell		*				
1980	CEGB 01 para 28.18 CEGB/S/78	Specification issued by BSI for a Total Quality Assurance Programme for nuclear power plants B.S. 5882					*	
1980	DTp/P/1 (App 2)	The Air Navigation Order 1980	*					(SI 1980 No. 1965) with reference to transport of radioactive material

DATE	SOURCE	EVENT	EVENT BY Govt	CEGB	BNFL	NNC	Other	COMMENT
1981 30 January	CEGB O1 para 1.6 CEGB O1 para 2.4	CEGB apply to Secretary of State for Energy for Section 2 consent and deemed planning permission. Form Bs sent to SCC and SCDC		*				
1981 30 January	CEGB O1 para 2.9	CEGB apply to NII for revision of existing Nuclear Site Licence (No 12A) to cover installation of PWR on Sizewell site		*				
1981 February	FOE Bundle 'A'	Project Statement issued		*				Statement issued publicly to provide preliminary information about the Sizewell B proposal
1981 13 February	CEGB/S/26	Select Committee on Energy Report on the Government's statement on the new nuclear power programme					*	
1981 April	Day 18 page 67D-F FOE/S/121	First Reference Design submitted to CEGB and rejected				*		
1981 May	CEGB/S/134	Monopolies and Mergers Commission Report on the operation by CEGB of its systems for the generation and supply of electricity in bulk					*	
1981 July	CEGB O1 para 16.15 DEN/S/2	Task Force (CEGB, NNC, Westinghouse, Bechtel, BNFL and UKAEA) set up. Announced to Parliament on 1 July		*		*		Task Force set up to arrive at satisfactory design for Sizewell PWR

DATE	SOURCE	EVENT	EVENT BY					COMMENT
			Govt	CEGB	BNFL	NNC	Other	
1981 15 July	Day 315 page 10B-11E	Written Parliamentary Answer by Secretary of State for Energy	*					NII claimed that this answer indicated that the Secretary of State was no longer committed to delaying the start of the Sizewell Inquiry until they were in posession of sufficient information to enable them to grant a licence. (See also Transcript Day 183, page 25 B-D and NII/P/1 (Add 4) page 35-36)
1981 22 July	CEGB 01 para 1.7	Secretary of State for Energy announces Sizewell B Public Inquiry	*					Included points regarded as relevant to the Inquiry
1981 July	CEGB/S/27	Government response (Cmnd 8317) to Select Committee on Energy's Report	*					
1981 August	Day 7 para 75D	CEGB and NNC sign agreement with SNUPPS organisation		*		*		Provided access to detailed information on SNUPPS design
1981	Day 48 page 36B-C	The Joint Project Team is set up		*		*		The team was set up in "Autumn 1981".
1981 September	CEGB 01 para 6.22	Completion of PWR Reference Design based on SNUPPS		*		*		Complied with NII programme (see NII 01, para 2.8)
1981 September	CEGB 01 para 16.1 Day 18, page 68E-F	The Sizewell B Reference Design is adopted by the CEGB and endorsed as the basis for further design work						

DATE	SOURCE	EVENT	EVENT BY Govt	CEGB	BNFL	NNC	Other	COMMENT
1981 17 September	NII 01 para 2.10 Day 264 page 17A-B Day 265 page 3F NII/P/2 (Add 19) pages 25-27	NII submit views to CEGB on main safety issues in new Reference Design					*	NII's views based on information available from CEGB and the Task Force. Letter contained 15 main points and detailed comments on 58 additional items
1981 22 September	NII 01 para 2.8 Day 183 page 103F	Revised programme of safety submissions agreed between CEGB (Task Force) and NII					*	This programme revised that agreed on 5.6.80 (qv). Main elements were (original dates in brackets if different):- mid-Dec '81 : first issue of draft PCSR (mid-Feb '81) to NII Dec '81-Mar '82: period of assessment by NII and discussion with CEGB May '82 : PCSR to be published (mid-Feb '82) July '82 : NII Review to be published (May '82)
1981 6 November	CEGB/S/16	Completed Form B sent by SCC to Department of Energy					*	Conveys views of Local Authority on CEGB's application
1981 16 December	CEGB 01 para 27.21 CEGB/S/84	Government announcement on policy on underground burial of radioactive waste	*					Drilling investigations discontinued since feasibility of underground burial established in principle, in light of review of work overseas

DATE	SOURCE	EVENT	EVENT BY					COMMENT
			Govt	CEGB	BNFL	NNC	Other	
1981 24 December	NII 01 para 2.8 Day183 page 10B	Draft PCSR submitted to NII	*					
1981	DTp/P/1 (App 2)	The Merchant Shipping (Dangerous Goods) Regulations 1981	*					(SI 1981 No.1747) with reference to transport of radioactive material
1981	CEGB 01 para 30.13	Amendment of Leiston/Aldeburgh Development (1961) and Outline (1962) Plans issued by Suffolk CC	*				*	
1982 20 January	CEGB 01 para 1.8	Secretary of State for Energy announces date for beginning of main hearings of the Inquiry	*					
1982 20 January	CI /74	Statement by HSE on the Inquiry	*					Public statement issued by HSE containing a statement by Mr Anthony, Chief Inspector of the NII, on "the role of NII in relation to the Inquiry and its view of the responsibility of the prospective licensee". NII Review of PCSR expected mid 1982. Will concentrate on major issues and indicate areas of reservation (Press notice first referred to by Counsel for NII on 23 January 1983 - Day 13,page 50F)

DATE	SOURCE	EVENT	EVENT BY					COMMENT
			Govt	CEGB	BNFL	NNC	Other	
1982 1 February	CEGB 01 para 6.15 DEN/S/2	Government Statement on programme for nuclear power stations	*					No commitment to programme beyond Heysham III and Sizewell B
1982 1 February	CEGB/S/17	Completed Form B sent by SCDC to Department of Energy					*	Conveys views of Local Authority on CEGB's application
1982 March	CEGB 01 para 19.2 CEGB/S/64	An assessment of the integrity of PWR pressure vessels. Second Report by Study Group chaired by Dr W Marshall (UKAEA)					*	
1982 March	CEGB 01 para 14.8 CEGB/S/52	Design Safety Criteria for CEGB nuclear power stations (revised) issued		*				Consolidates advice on safety requirements for all types of future stations
1982 April	CEGB 01 para 14.49 CEGB/S/53	Publication of PWR Design Safety Guidelines		*				More detailed guide to designers on the implementation of the criteria for PWRs in the Design Safety Criteria
1982 April	CEGB 01 CEGB 02	CEGB issue Statement of Case, Pre-Construction Safety Report and revised Reference Design		*				
1982 1 June	Trancripts	Inquiry Preliminary Meetings						
1982 11 June	SB 5	Notice of formal opening of Inquiry on 26.7.82 and Secretary of State for Energy's 'Rule 5' statement	*					Notice of formal opening of Inquiry and of points which the Secretary of State considers relevant, in accordance with rules 4(10) and 5(1) of the Electricity Generating Stations and Overhead Lines (Inquiry Procedure) Rules 1981

DATE	SOURCE	EVENT	EVENT BY					COMMENT
			Govt	CEGB	BNFL	NNC	Other	
1982 July	Day 47 page 48G-49B	Guide to the administration of the Radioactive Substances Act 1960	*					Reflects conclusions of the DOE Review published in 1979 (qv) of Cmnd 884 (1959) (qv)
1982 July	NII 01	Publication of NII Review of PCSR					*	
1982 July	Day 47 page 57D-F	BNFL given planning permission for construction of a vitrification plant at Sellafield	*					Will convert existing stored liquid wastes to borosilicate glass blocks within metal containers. Expected to come into operation in 1987
1982 18 July	SB 20	Letter from Inspector to Secretary of State for Energy about funding of objectors					*	Reply: see SB 21, letter of 21.9.82 (qv)
1982 22 July	Day 8 page 7F CEGB/S/142	"Radioactive waste management" (Cmnd 8607)	*					
1982 26-27 July	Days 1+2	Formal opening of Inquiry						
1982 21 September	SB 21	Reply from Secretary of State for Energy to Inspector on funding of objectors	*					Inspector's letter: see SB 20, letter of 18.7.82 (qv)
1982 18+19 Oct	Day 3 + 4	Final 2 days of Inquiry before main hearing						
1982 19 October	Day 4 page 9A	Counsel for the NII tells Inquiry that Mr Dunster's hope that NII will be in a position effectively to license Sizewell B before Inquiry is 'incapable of realisation'					*	Mr Dunster's views explained on 26 March 1980 (qv)

DATE	SOURCE	EVENT	EVENT BY Govt	CEGB	BNFL	NNC	Other	COMMENT
1982 9 November	Day 182 page 74E-G	Contract design defined. Agreed between NII and CEGB						
1982 November	NII 01 Supp 1	Publication of NII supplement on degraded core analysis					*	Supplement to NII 01 - NII's Review of PCSR
1982 December	NII 01 Supp 2	Publication of NII Supplement on Safety analysis					*	Supplement to NII 01 - NII's Review of PCSR
1982	Day 47 page 47G-48C	Nuclear Industry Radioactive Waste Executive (NIREX) set up		*	*			Members are BNFL, CEGB, UKAEA and SSEB
1982	Day 191 page 7E	Report of ACSNI (Advisory Committee on the Safety of Nuclear Installations) sub-committee published					*	Includes a report by ACSNI's PWR study group on primary pressure circuit integrity
1982	Day 191 page 7F-G	UKAEA pressure vessel defect detection trials					*	
1983 11 January	Transcript Day 5	Main hearings of Inquiry begin						
1983 January	NII 01 Supps 5 & 6	Publication of NII Supplements on fuel clad ballooning and on reactor protection system					*	Supplements to NII 01 - NII's Review of PCSR
1983 March	NII 01 Supps 3, 4, 7 & 8	Publication of NII Supplements on: external hazards-aircraft crash, earthquake, fire; and steam generator tube integrity					*	Supplements to NII 01 - NII's Review of PCSR

DATE	SOURCE	EVENT	Govt	CEGB	BNFL	NNC	Other	COMMENT
1983 April	CEGB/P/8 (Add 4 Rev) Table 3	Dungeness B (AGR) station: first reactor comes on stream		*				Station ordered in 1965 (qv)
1983 July	NII 01 Supps 9, 10, 11, 12, 13 & 14	Publication of NII Supplements on: code validation for LOCA, reactor pressure vessel, pressure circuit components, ALARP strategy for dose reduction, human factors and quality assurance					*	Supplements to NII 01 - NII's Review of PCSR
1984 February	Day 315 page 80D-G CEGB/S/975	Publication of Tackling Pollution - Experience and Prospects (Tenth Report of Royal Commission on Environmental Pollution) (CMND 9149)	*					
1984 20 April	Day 211 page 4H-5C	Unit 4 of DRAX commissioned		*				This represents a construction period of 62 months from start of main foundations
1984 22 May	NII/P/2 (Add 9) page 8-11	Letter from Rimmington (DG-HSE) to Marshall (Chairman-CEGB) on the way licensing discussions proceeding					*	First letter in Rimmington/Marshall correspondence 'in light of concerns expressed by the Inspector', proposing a review of the 'nature and method of the dialogue' between NII and CEGB
1984 25 June	NII/P/2 (Add 9) page 8-11	Rimmington - Marshall letter following review by NII and CEGB of 'nature and method of the dialogue' between them					*	Revised structure of meetings agreed for resolving safety issues. (238 days of Inquiry had passed by this time)

EVENT BY

LIST OF MEETINGS NOT FORMING PART OF THE INQUIRY

(a) LOCAL EVENING MEETINGS

Venue	Date	Purpose
1. Yoxford Village Hall	19 Oct 1983	Called following a request from Middleton-cum-Fordley, Theberton and Eastbridge,and Yoxford Parish Councils (known at the Inquiry as the Joint Parish Councils) for an opportunity for local residents to express their opinions to the Inspector.
2. Leiston Film Theatre	30 Nov 1983	Response to a request from Leiston Town Council for an opportunity for local residents to express their opinions to the Inspector.
3. Leiston Film Theatre	15 Nov 1984	Opportunity for local residents to question CEGB and Local Planning Authority witnesses, and express their own opinions, on the CEGB's plans for the construction of Sizewell B. The meeting was called following the submission of evidence by the CEGB in the Autumn of 1984 which enabled an assessment to be made of the likely impact of its proposals and the possible consequences for local residents.

(b) SIDE-ROOM MEETINGS

Subject Under Discussion	Date of Meeting
1. Computer programmes used to support the economic case for Sizewell B	21 Dec 1982
2. The CEGB's generating security standard	6 Jan 1983
3. Information on the economics of Sizewell B	26 Jan 1983
4. Code Validation	10 Feb 1983
5. PWR siting	3 March 1983
6. Transport of irradiated nuclear fuel	14 March 1983
7. Project/Site Management for Sizewell B	15 June 1983
8. Use of the CERG model	22 June 1983
9. Further information on the economics of Sizewell B	21 July 1983
10. CERG model: initial results and future programme of work	28 July 1983
11. CERG model: next phase in programme of work	10 Oct 1983

(b) **SIDE-ROOM MEETINGS (Continued)**

Subject Under Discussion	Date of Meeting
12. Comparison of Fossil Fuel Price Projections	31 Oct 1983
13. Results of CERG probabilistic analysis	13 April 1984
14. Emergency Plan: proposed examination	5 June 1984
15. CERG model: matters arising out of the CEGB's comments on the sensitivity test results in INQ/77	7 Dec 1984

LIST OF SITE INSPECTIONS

Date	Sites Visited	
2 May 1984	PWR site at Paluel, France.	Accompanied
3 May 1984	PWR site at Tihange, Belgium.	Accompanied
11 July 1984	Kenton Hills and Goose Hill (immediately to north and north west of Sizewell site). Local roads in Sternfield, Saxmundham, Yoxford, Middleton Moor, Theberton, Eastbridge and Leiston.	Unaccompanied
11 October 1984	The land over which the proposed routes for the new private access road to Sizewell B would pass (see Fig 97.1).	Unaccompanied
23 January 1985	Routes between Sizewell and the potential sources of aggregate in the Blyth and Waveney valleys.	Unaccompanied
18 April 1985	The Sizewell site. The land over which the proposed routes for the new private access road would pass including Sizewell Belts, Goose Hill, Kenton Hills, Leiston Common, Sandy Lane, Broom Covert, Rookyard Wood, Coronation Wood and the land between the C228 from Crown Lodge to Sizewell Gap and the site.	Accompanied
19 April 1985	Local roads, including: C228 (Lovers Lane); B1122; A12 between Wickham Market and Blythburgh; A1120 between Yoxford and Stowmarket; B1078 between Otley and Wickham Market; and the three other minor roads linking the A12 with Leiston (see Fig 94.2)	Accompanied
4 June 1985	Control room at Hinkley Point B Power Station. Access road and emergency routes on site.	
11 June 1985	Access roads to Dungeness Power Station site.	Accompanied
18 June 1985	Access roads and prescribed construction traffic routeing to Heysham Power Station site.	Accompanied
3 September 1985	Inspection of the B1122 at harvest-time.	Accompanied

Correspondence Between the Inspector and the
Secretary of State for Energy About the
Funding of Objectors

(Issued as Inquiry Documents SB20 and SB21)

2, MITRE COURT BUILDINGS
TEMPLE,
EC4Y 7BX.
TELEPHONE: 01-583 1355.

18th July, 1982.

The Rt. Hon. Nigel Lawson,
Secretary of State for Energy,
Department of Energy,
Thames House, South.Millbank,
S.W.1.P. 4Q.J.
LONDON.

Dear Secretary of State;

THE SIZEWELL INQUIRY

On the 1st June I held a preliminary meeting for the Sizewell
Inquiry which lasted for three days.   During the meeting the most frequent
request made to me was for the provision of public funds to objectors and
others who wish to appear at the Inquiry.   These requests came from
individuals and interested groups of many kinds and corporate bodies such
as Trade Unions and local authorities.   It was clear to me that these
requests reflected strongly and widely held views which, in many instances,
were based on thoughtful and well-considered arguments.

Many of those present at the meeting asked me to pass on their
arguments to you and this I now seek to do.   In doing so, I realise that
requests of a similar kind have been drawn to the attention of Ministers
on a number of previous occasions; the Report of Mr. Justice Parker on the
Windscale Inquiry (paragraphs 15.8 & 15.9) is a prominent instance. However,
the correspondence regarding Sizewell between objectors and yourself and

Page 2/..

your Ministerial colleagues has plainly left some of those objectors with the feeling that they have been unsuccessful in putting their arguments sufficiently effectively or clearly to Ministers.   They complain that the Government's replies show that their requests have not been fully understood or considered.

The representations I now put before you raise questions that extend well beyond my scope and knowledge as your Inspector for the Sizewell Inquiry.   I therefore make no recommendations to you about the provision of financial assistance to objectors.   However, because of the extent, character and importance of the representations and the extent of considered feeling they reflect, I ask that the provision of financial assistance be reconsidered.

Those advising you will have seen the transcripts of the three-day meeting and can identify any special or particular reference for you. I attach to this letter a representative list of those who made relevant requests, with the key transcript references, should you or your advisers wish to look at the precise terms employed by those requesting assistance.

Before I summarise the principal arguments I was asked to convey to you, I draw attention to the distinction made as to the Scale of Finance help sought.   The main weight of contention was addressed to the need to prepare an adequate case and its presentation at the Inquiry. Others, however, were content to seek the payment of 'expenses', meaning mainly the cost of travelling and accommodation incurred by a Party in order to attend the main hearing and its preliminary meetings.   Some of

Page 3/..

those who sought preparation and presentation costs, would if refused part
or all of those costs, still contend strongly for their expenses to be paid.

The two principal arguments for financial assistance can be
expressed shortly.   First, the subjects to be examined at the Inquiry are
of great national importance, especially those of Energy Policy, and concern
actions and consequences that will extend over a long span of years.   Some
of the subjects involved are highly complex and technical whose understanding
requires much work in fields bordering on the edge of existing knowledge.
Some subjects, such as risks to human health and safety, have aroused wide-
spread public concern.   The financial implications of the proposals under
scrutiny are very large, wideranging and have important repercussions.
These aspects taken together, it was strongly urged, mean that the Sizewell
Inquiry is a unique, at at least special, case so far as the provision of
public funds is concerned.

Secondly, it was stressed that the likelihood is the Inquiry
will be the sole opportunity which the public will have to take part in a
critical examination of the national issues involved.   It was argued that,
if Sizewell B is permitted, all future Inquiries into P.W.R.Stations will
be concerned, wholly or mainly with siting and local environmental aspects
only.

Taken together, these two propositions mean that objectors
must be in a position to carry out enough work, including research work, to
enable them to advance an adequately critical case at the Inquiry.   The
very substantial documentation being provided by the CEGB and the N I I needs

4.

to be most carefully examined and considered, often with expert assistance, fully to understand the material if a response of any value is to be made to it at the Inquiry.   That, it was stressed, cannot be done without sub-stantial expense.   That last point reflects Mr. Justice Parker's observation: "There can nevertheless be no doubt that the costs of presenting a fully developed case at the Inquiry and, equally investigating the validity of the appellants' case are very considerable" (para 15.9).   It is the need to "investigate the validity" of the CEGB case that, as I understand it, lies at the heart of the objectors' requests to you.

Great emphasis was laid upon the disparity between the immense financial outlay in preparation for the Inquiry by the CEGB, N I I, BNFL, Bechtel, Westinghouse and other supporting parties and that which will be available to opponents in the absence of financial assistance to objectors from public funds.   They say that, apart from making their position very weak, the effects of that disparity will render it impossible for the Inquiry to have the characteristics of being "full, fair and thorough", which you wish it to have, both in appearance and in reality.   From a purely technical point of view, it was asserted that P.W.R. technology will not be "put under the microscope" at the Inquiry as Ministers should wish.   To enable that to be done by or with the assistance of objectors would cost a small fraction of the preparation costs of the proponents.

It was recognised by most objectors that if the Government were to grant their request in principle there remain problems about the distri-bution and use of the money provided.   Two approaches were made to the practical problem.   First, my attention was drawn to the way in which such difficulties had been successfully met in Canada in regard to the Mackenzie Valley Pipeline Inquiry.   (The way in which it was handled is set out in the transcript for 1st June at pp 67-68).   It was considered there was no serious obstacle to adopting a similar approach in this country.

Secondly, while evidently accepting that no one would ever be entirely satisfied, effective and cooperative arrangements could readily be achieved to ensure fair distribution and proper use of any monies made available.

Critical comment was addressed to the reasons given by Ministers, in correspondence, for resisting requests for financial assistance.   These were succinctly and lucidly summarised by Mr. Howell of counsel, appearing for the Friends of the Earth.   I cannot do better than to attach an extract from the transcript of the 2nd June (pp 24-27) in which he states the response to Ministers' reasoning, and ask you to regard that extract as part of this letter.

The great majority of those who made representations to me did so on the basis of the contentions I have summarised above.   A number of objectors went further and maintained that a failure to provide financial assistance might, sooner or later, have unfortunate political or social consequences.   They based their warning on the belief that in the absence of financial assistance, the Inquiry would be seen, or believed to have been, an ineffective or insufficient critical examination of the proposals.

Throughout I have referred to objectors, for brevity, but the

word is intended to include all parties who sought financial help.   But
two parties who supported the pleas for such assistance represented those
who support the CEGB proposals.   Doubtless, there will be other supporters
who will wish to seek financial help if the request is granted in principle.

This letter is long and a tax on your time.   In view of the
considerable feeling and interest in the request I have reported and the
anxiety to ensure that no misunderstanding could be reasonably thought to
remain in Ministers' minds about the basis and nature of the request, I
have sought to cover in outline the main arguments in this letter.   As you
and your colleagues will, I hope, be willing to reconsider the objectors'
requests I am sending this letter to you and Sir Donald Maitland only.   At
a convenient later time, I hope you may agree to this letter becoming an
Inquiry document.

Yours faithfully,

Frank Layfield

Sir Frank Layfield, Q.C.

Copy to : Sir Donald Maitland, G.C.M.G., O.B.E.,
          Permanent Under-Secretary of State.

Enclosures:
1.   Representative list of relevant requests
      together with the key transcript references.

2.   Mackenzie Valley Pipeline Inquiry -
      transcript for 1st June at pp 67-68.

3.   Friends of the Earth -
      Extract from the transcript of 2nd June (pp 24-27)

Sir Frank Layfield QC
2 Mitre Court Buildings
Temple
London
EC4Y 7BX

21 September 1982

[signature]

THE SIZEWELL INQUIRY

Thank you for your letter of 18 July, inviting me to reconsider t
question of financial aid to third parties. I recognise the
sincerity and care with which the case for such aid has been put
and I am grateful to you for setting out the arguments so fully a
so fairly.

I have read your letter and its enclosures very carefully and
reconsidered all the arguments. These are not much different fro
those which I examined before making my views known to Parliamen
on 1 February 1982 (Official Report Cols 25, 26). I am still not
persuaded that the lack of financial assistance by the Government
will make it impossible for the Inquiry to be "full, fair and
thorough".

The arguments fall into two main groups. The first is that the
complex technical and financial issues involved are so important
nationally as to make the Sizewell Inquiry unique. It is argued
that this will be the only opportunity to examine these issues
directly in relation to the PWR.

Counsel for my Department commented on this proposition at the
formal opening of the Inquiry on 26 July. Any future application
for a nuclear power station will be judged on its own merits. Li
Sizewell, future inquiries under Section 34 of the Electricity Ac
1957 must conform both to the provisions of that section and to
the Electricity Generating Stations and Overhead Lines (Inquiries
Procedure) Rules 1981 made last December. These rules require
from the Secretary of State a written statement of the points whi
he thinks relevant to his consideration of a power station application. This is for the guidance of the Inspector but it is not
binding on him. The scope of the evidence to be heard at a futur

nquiry is a matter for the Inspector appointed to conduct it.
s complete freedom to decide what evidence he wishes to hear
annot be limited in advance in any way. So, although this Inquiry
 a first opportunity to consider and evaluate the issues, it is
t the only one.

r am I persuaded that giving financial assistance at Sizewell
uld be accepted as a special case, not constituting a precedent.
 have in mind in particular those with interests in major planning
quiries in future. If giving aid at Sizewell did lead to state
nding of objectors (let alone other interested parties) in future,
e extra costs to the public purse could be very large. I do not
lieve that this would be in the national interest. I would also
int out that considerable sums have already been committed to
afeguard the public interest. First, there is the cost of the
quiry itself. Second, the Nuclear Installations Inspectorate
II) has already spent some £7m in evaluating the PWR design since
974. Its report of 15 July on the CEGB's pre-construction safety
port alone cost £200,000.   Its current rate of expenditure on
WR safety work is £2m a year. Not only objectors, but also the
axpayer has an interest in the conduct of public inquiries. The
overnment must have regard to both interests. It also has to
ecide whether such public funds as are available are best applied
 rigorous independent scrutiny or to the financing of interested
arties and pressure groups.

e general view of the Government remains that organisations and
dividuals making representations at public inquiries can reasonably
 expected to meet their own costs. This applies to both categories
f costs which you describe at the end of page 2 of your letter.

e second group of arguments for financial help is that objectors
ed it to command expert advice. This is to master the substantial
cumentation provided by the CEGB and the NII so as to investigate
horoughly the validity of the CEGB's case. The disparity of
inancial resources between objectors and the CEGB and other supportin
arties is part of this argument.

his seems to me to undervalue the contribution which the NII itself
ill make. It is a totally independent body. The job it has been
oing and will continue to do on nuclear safety is to put the
echnology under the microscope. It then advises its parent body,
e Health and Safety Executive (HSE). The HSE, with this advice,
ecides whether a licence can be granted for the construction and
peration of a nuclear reactor. It also safeguards the health and
afety both of those who may be employed in building and operating
e reactor and of the public at large. The NII is uniquely
quipped with the resources and expertise to make a thorough and
ndependent examination of the safety issues surrounding the proposed
izewell installation. Its report is itself a valuable independent
id to all parties wishing to probe and discuss the safety aspects
f the project.

In addition, the statutory provisions governing the Inquiry are themselves designed to safeguard the general public interest, including the interests of objectors. You yourself have been selected as an independent and highly qualified Inspector. You will be advised by equally independent and expert Assessors, who will help to ensure that the CEGB's application is thoroughly tested. I have decided to appoint three Assessors, with specific expertise in relation to the biological effects of radiation, the engineering aspects and/economics of the CEGB's case for the Sizewell PWR.

I am satisfied that these arrangements do provide a full and proper opportunity for the evaluation of the CEGB's proposals, taking account of any relevant points or doubts which objectors may express.

For the reasons set out in this letter I am not disposed to change my previous decision.

I am happy to agree that your letter and mine should become Inquiry documents. I also intend to make them available to all Members of Parliament.

NIGEL LAWSON

INQUIRY SECRETARIAT

The duration of the Inquiry and Report writing inevitably meant that many people were with the Secretariat for only part of the time. Members of the Secretariat included:

Dr D P Hauser   Inquiry Secretary

Mr J P Clayton
Mr R Davies
Miss P F Henderson
Mr C T Matthews
Mr K C Price
Dr K W Rutledge
Mrs E H Taylor
Mr C J C Wright

Miss L A E Boyd
Mr L J Cadman
Mr J Crowe   Documents Officer
Mr M A Euesden
Mr G A Ewart
Mr S J Haffenden
Mr K J R Parker   Indexer
Mr J Regan
Mr M P Seeney
Mr K R Smith   Programme Officer

Mr R C Bastable
Mr L Eggleton
Miss D Hocking
Miss R J Revell
Miss P M Yeates

Miss C J Houchin   Inspector's Personal Secretary
Miss G C Marson
Miss T A Smith

Mr J Dickson   )
Mr M J Harris   )   Assistance to Assessors
Mr D Stafford   )

COUNSEL TO THE INQUIRY

Mr H Brooke QC
Mr A J Kolodziej
Mr A J Sandal   )   Treasury Solicitor's Department
Mr S A Mohammed   )

TRANSCRIPT WRITERS

J L Harphams Ltd

LIST OF APPEARANCES

CENTRAL ELECTRICITY GENERATING BOARD (CEGB)

ADVOCATES

LORD SILSOE, QC
MR MICHAEL FITZGERALD, QC
MR GEORGE BARTLETT, of Counsel
MR NICHOLAS BURTON, of Counsel

Instructed By:

MR M G HERBERT, Solicitor

WITNESSES

Witness Proof of Evidence	Qualifications & Position	Days of Appearance
MR J W BAKER CEGB/P/1 CEGB/P/46	MA; Board Member	7-8, 63-74, 285; 234-235
MR R R MATTHEWS CEGB/P/2 Supported by: Mr P A Corkerton	MA, CEng, FIMechE, FIEE; Director of Health and Safety Head of Engineering Group, Health and Safety Department(HSD)	8-9, 155-157, 162-165 155-157, 162-165
DR J K WRIGHT CEGB/P/3 CEGB/P/9	MA, DSc, FInstP, MIEE; Director, Technology Planning and Research Division	9-10, 74-75, 115-118; 17-18, 126
MR F P JENKIN CEGB/P/4	MA; Development Strategy Engineer, Corporate Strategy Department	10-11, 84, 98, 105-106, 136-137, 239-240, 306
MR C H DAVIES CEGB/P/5	BA, MSc(Econ); Head of Economic Policy Section, Corporate Strategy Department	11-12, 14, 76-77, 96, 107-109
MR P R HUGHES CEGB/P/6	HND, MIElecIE; Manager, Fossil Fuel and Energy Section	13-14, 77-79, 88, 96-97, 119-121
MR M TOWNSEND CEGB/P/7	DipEEng, MIEE, FBIM; Head of British Civil Uranium Procurement Organisation	14-15, 106

Witness Proof of Evidence	Qualifications & Position	Days of Appearance
MR A WILSON CEGB/P/8	CEng, MICE; Planning and Technical Services Engineeer	15-17, 79-82, 97-98, 121-124
Supported by: Mr R A Flint	CEng, FIEE, FIERE; Manager, NNC Project Control Services Department	16-17, 121-122
Mr D G Marshall	FInstPM, FIIM, FBIM; Head of Industrial Relations Branch, Generation Development and Construction Division (GDCD)	121-122
Mr J D McFarlane	CEng, FIEE; Manager, NNC Construction Division	16-17, 121-122
Mr D Norman	MIS; Principal Engineer, GDCD	121-122
MR B V GEORGE CEGB/P/10	BTech, CEng, MIMechE; Director of the PWR	18-20, 124-125, 176, 193-195, 197, 204, 206, 220-221, 307;
CEGB/P/32 (replacing Dr L M C Dutton) CEGB/P/47		217-218; 235-238
Supported by: Mr A J Joyce (P/10)	NNC staff member	176, 193-195
Mr R Mannion (P/10)	NNC staff member	176, 193-195, 197, 220-221
Mr I G Pugh (P/32)	BSc; Head of Radiation and Physics Group, GDCD	217-218
Mr J D McFarlane (P/47)	CEng, FIEE; Manager, NNC Construction Division	235-238
Mr J L Elston (P/47)	CEng, FIEE; Project Manager, Sizewell B Project Management Team	235-237
MR J R HARRISON CEGB/P/11	BSc; Head of New Projects Section, HSD	23-25, 169-173, 202, 204, 206, 261-263;
CEGB/P/45		35-36, 169-173
Supported by: Mr P A Corkerton	Head of Engineering Group, HSD	169-173, 202, 204, 206, 261-263
Mr C J Dunnicliffe	NNC staff member	169-173, 262-263
Mr J E Sell	NNC staff member	169-173, 262-263
DR B EDMONDSON CEGB/P/12	DMet; Director, Nuclear Operations Support Group	22-23, 190-192, 202-203, 207, 243
Supported by: Mr D P Luckhurst	BEng; Head of Primary Equipment, NNC PWR Joint Project Team	190-192, 202-203

Witness Proof of Evidence	Qualifications & Position	Days of Appearance
DR M J WHITTLE CEGB/13	BSc, PhD; Head of Non-Destructive Testing (NDT) Applications Centre	22-23, 190-192 202-203
Supported by: Dr J Tomlinson	BA, PhD; Head of NDT Developments Section, NDT Applications Centre	190-192, 202-203
PROF G P SMEDLEY CEGB/P/14	BME, BMet, FEng, FIM, FWeldI, MIMechE; Deputy Chief Engineer Surveyor, Lloyd's Register of Shipping	23, 190-192
Supported by: Mr D P Luckhurst	BEng; NNC PWR Joint Project Team	190-192
MR J E NEWELL CEGB/P/15	BSc, CEng, FIChemE, ARCSc; Nuclear Boiler Engineer, GDCD	20-21, 192
Supported by: Dr J Tomlinson	BA, PhD; NDT Applications Centre	192
DR J H GITTUS CEGB/P/16	DSc, DTech, BSc, FIMechE, FIM, FInstP, FInstS; Director, UKAEA PWR Safety Research Programme	29-30, 166-168, 211-215
Supported by: Mr F P O Ashworth	BSc, MSc, FInstP; Head of Safety Analysis Co-ordination, NNC PWR Project Team	166-168, 211-214
Dr M R Hayns	BSc, PhD, FInstP; Member of UKAEA Safety and Reliability Directorate	166-168, 211-215
Mr M J Hitchler	BSc, MMechE, MASME; Probabilistic Risk Assessment Group Manager, Westinghouse Nuclear Centre	166-168, 211-214
Dr G N Kelly	BSc, PhD; Staff member, NRPB Assessment Department	166-168, 211-214
Mr N J Liparulo	BSc, MMechE; Core, Containment and Consequence Analysis Group Manager, Westinghouse Electric Corporation	166-168, 211-213
DR J A L BONNELL CEGB/P/17	BMed, BS, FFOM, FRSM; Medical Adviser to CEGB and Electricity Council	31, 229
Supported by: Dr R A Cartwright	MA, BMed, BS, PhD, MFCM; Consultant Epidemiologist to Yorkshire RHA and CEGB	229
Dr G A Harte	MA, PhD; Research Worker, Health Physics Research Station, Berkeley Nuclear Laboratories	229
MR R B PEPPER CEGB/P/18	BSc, MInstP; Principal Health Physicist	31-32, 221-222

Witness Proof of Evidence	Qualifications & Position	Days of Appearance
MR P T McINERNEY CEGB/P/19 Supported by:	CEng, MIEE, MIMechE, FBIM; Director of Production, South Eastern Region	30-31, 219-221
Mr R H Pope	BSc; Head of Ergonomics Sub-group, GDCD	220-221
MR F H PASSANT CEGB/P/20	HNC; Head of Active Waste Project, GDCD	32-34, 201, 271-272
DR R H FLOWERS CEGB/P/21	BSc, PhD; Fuel Processing Director, UKAEA	34, 201, 271-272
DR G J WOMACK CEGB/P/22	MScTech, PhD, CEng, FInstE, MIChemE, MIEE, MInstP; Principal Engineer, Plant Engineering Department, GDCD	34-35, 209, 250-254
MR L SINGLETON CEGB/P/23	Traffic Manager, British Railways Board	35, 251
MR A R GREGORY CEGB/P/24	BEng, CEng, FIEE; Principal Engineer, Plant Engineering Department, GDCD	35, 201-202, 273
MR K M GAMMON CEGB/P/25 Supported by:	BSc, CEng, FICE, FBIM; Generation Development Engineer, Corporate Strategy Department	36-37, 247-250, 286-287
Mr J D McFarlane	CEng, FIEE; Manager, NNC Construction Division	286-287
Mr G W Barrett	BSc, MSc; Group Head, Technology Planning Research Division	287
MR P J ARNOLD CEGB/P/27	BEngSc, CEng, MIEE; Transmission Development Engineer	36, 248-250
MR W T MAWER CEGB/P/28	BSc; Mechanical Engineer, Station Design Department, GDCD	37
MR F B HAWES CEGB/P/29	BSc; Biological Adviser, Generation Studies Branch	37
MR B HENDERSON CEGB/P/30	FRIBA, FSIAD; Senior Partner, Yorke Rosenberg Mardall, Architects and Planners	37, 288
MR P YOUNGMAN CEGB/P/31 Supported by:	PPILA, FRTPI; Consultant landscape architect	37-38, 288
Dr D S Ranwell	BSc, PhD; Honorary Reader, University of East Anglia School of Biological Sciences (formerly head of NCC's Coastal Ecology Research Station, Norwich)	288

- 4 -

Witness Proof of Evidence	Qualifications & Position	Days of Appearance

DR L M C DUTTON
    CEGB/P/32
    CEGB/P/33
	BSc, PhD; Head of NNC Radiological
	Protection Group
		21-22;
		25-26

Later: MR B V GEORGE (P/32)	BTech, CEng, MIMechE; Director of the PWR	217-218
MR I G PUGH (P/33)	BSc; Head of Radiation and Physics Group, GDCD	218-219
DR P R FARMER CEGB/P/34	BSc, Phd; Head of Fluid Dynamics Section, Central Electricity Research Laboratories	26-28, 161, 173-175, 246-247
Supported by: Mr K T Routledge	Head of LOCA Analysis Section, NNC	173-175, 246-247
DR T HEALEY CEGB/P/37	BSc, PhD; Head of Mechanical Properties Section, Berkeley Nuclear Laboratories	28, 175, 246-247
and DR S J BOARD CEGB/P/37	BSc, PhD; Head of Thermal Hydraulic Safety Studies Section, Berkeley Nuclear Laboratories	28, 175, 246-247
Supported by: Mr K T Routledge	Head of LOCA Analysis Section, NNC	175, 246-247
MR D W ANDERSON CEGB/P/39	BSc; Senior Engineer, Reactor Technology Section, GDCD	17, 109
MR D A WARD CEGB/P/43	BA; Assistant Manager, NNC PWR Systems and Safety Department	26, 161, 175-176 246-247
Supported by: Mr K T Routledge	Head of LOCA Analysis Section, NNC	175-176, 246-247
DR A VIGNES CEGB/P/44	DScA; Technical Director, Framatome & Co. Manufacturing Division	27, 190-192
Supported by: Mr D P Luckhurst	BEng; NNC PWR Joint Project Team	190-192

BRITISH NUCLEAR FUELS PLC (BNFL)

ADVOCATES

MR GERARD RYAN, QC
MR ROBIN BARRATT, of Counsel
MS J WHITEAR, of Counsel

Instructed By:

Mr P D GREEN, Chief Legal Adviser

WITNESSES

Witness Proof of Evidence	Qualifications & Position	Days of Appearance
DR D G AVERY BNFL/P/1	BSc, PhD, FInstP; Deputy Managing Director	39, 125, 274-276
Supported by: Mr W Melling	Manager, Commercial Directorate Programmes Office	274
Mr H Sturman	Head of External and Technical Services	274
Mr R Dodds	Head of Long Term Planning, Reprocessing Division	274-276
Mr S T Hermiston	BSc; Former Manager, Sellafield Health Physics Services	274-276

NATIONAL NUCLEAR CORPORATION (NNC)

ADVOCATES

MR MICHAEL MANN, QC (now Mr Justice Mann)
Later:
MR JOHN DRINKWATER, QC
MR KEITH LINDBLOM, of Counsel

Instructed By:

MR F L ASHMAN, Company Secretary

WITNESSES

Witness Proof of Evidence	Qualifications & Position	Days of Appearance
DR N L FRANKLIN, OBE NNC/P/1	PhD, FRS, FEng; Managing Director	48
Later: MR C E PUGH	CEng, MIMechE; Managing Director (formerly NNC Director in charge of	290-291
NNC/P/2	Joint Project Team and Director of CEGB)	48-49, 291
Supported by: Mr J R M Southwood (P/1)	BSc, FIMechE, MIEE; Engineering Director	48
Mr J D McKean (P/1)	BSc; Manager, Research and Development Division	48
Mr W A K Wicks	FICA; Finance Director	48, 290-291
Mr R A Flint	CEng, FIEE, FIERE; Manager, Project Control Services Department	290-291
Mr D R Smith	MA, FEng; Director of PWR and Engineering	290-291

LOCAL PLANNING AUTHORITIES

SUFFOLK COUNTY COUNCIL AND SUFFOLK COASTAL DISTRICT COUNCIL (LPAs)

ADVOCATES

MR MICHAEL RICH, QC
MR DAVID HANDS, of Counsel

Instructed By:

SUFFOLK COUNTY COUNCIL and SUFFOLK COASTAL DISTRICT COUNCIL

WITNESSES

Witness Proof of Evidence	Qualifications & Position	Days of Appearance
MR E E BARRITT LPA/P/1 Supported by:	MA, MA, DipTP, MRTPI; County Planning Officer	63, 291-293, 303
Mr S Grimwade	DipTP, MRTPI; Development Planning Officer, Suffolk Coastal District Council	291-293, 303
Mr D W Ayre	BA, MRTPI; Assistant County Planning Officer (Policy)	291-293
Mr J P Girling	CEng, MICE; Deputy County Surveyor	291-293, 303
Mr J R Pegler	Surveyor's Department, Suffolk County Council	293
MR K RATCLIFFE LPA/P/2	BSc, CEng, MIMechE, FIOA; Senior Consultant, Wolfson Unit for Noise and Vibration Control	53
PROF D C LESLIE LPA/P/3	MA, DPhil, CEng, FInstNucE; Professor of Nuclear Engineering, University of London, and Dean of the Faculty of Engineering, Queen Mary College	59-60, 198
PROF K F KUSSMAUL LPA/P/4	Dr-Ing; Professor of Materials Testing, Materials Science and Structural Science, University of Stuttgart, and Director of the State Laboratory for the Testing of Materials	61-62
DR R S SAYLES LPA/P/5	BEng, PhD; Head of Tribology, Mechanical Engineering Department, Imperial College, London	62, 199

LICENSING AUTHORITY

HM NUCLEAR INSTALLATIONS INSPECTORATE (NII)

ADVOCATES

MR MICHAEL HOWARD, QC
Later:
MR NIGEL MACLEOD, QC
MR DAVID HOLGATE, of Counsel

Instructed By:

TREASURY SOLICITOR

WITNESSES

Witness Proof of Evidence	Qualifications & Position	Days of Appearance
MR R D ANTHONY NII/P/1 Supported by:	HM Chief Inspector of Nuclear Installations	56, 59, 158-161, 183, 270, 278
Mr J Locke	Formerly Director General, Health and Safety Executive	158-161, 183
Mr J D Rimington	Director General, Health and Safety Executive	278
Dr S A Harbison	HM Superintending Inspector of Nuclear Installations	158-161, 183, 278
Mr W S Gronow	HM Deputy Chief Inspector of Nuclear Installations	160, 270
MR P B WOODS NII/P/2 Supported by:	HM Deputy Chief Inspector of Nuclear Installations	57-59, 182-184, 188, 196, 204, 206, 215, 263-265, 307
Mr T Currie	HM Superintending Inspector of Nuclear Installations	182-184, 196, 206, 263-265
Mr J L Petrie	HM Superintending Inspector of Nuclear Installations	182-184, 196, 204, 206, 264-265
Mr J F Campbell	HM Principal Inspector of Nuclear Installations	182-184, 265
Mr A Edwards	HM Superintending Inspector of Nuclear Installations	204
Dr S A Harbison	HM Superintending Inspector of Nuclear Installations	215, 263

GOVERNMENT DEPARTMENTS AND ADVISORY BODIES

DEPARTMENT OF ENERGY (DEN)

ADVOCATES

MR JEREMY SULLIVAN, QC
MR JUSTIN FENWICK

Instructed By:

TREASURY SOLICITOR

WITNESSES

Witness Proof of Evidence	Qualifications & Position	Days of Appearance
MR R J PRIDDLE DEN/P/1	Under-Secretary, Head of Energy Policy Division	40-47
Suppported by: Dr K J Wigley	Senior Economic Adviser	40-47

DEPARTMENT OF THE ENVIRONMENT (DOE)

DEPARTMENT OF TRANSPORT (DTp)

MINISTRY OF AGRICULTURE, FISHERIES AND FOOD (MAFF)

ADVOCATE

MR CHRISTOPHER SYMONS, of Counsel

Instructed By:

TREASURY SOLICITOR

DOE WITNESSES

Witness Proof of Evidence	Qualifications & Position	Days of Appearance
MR G WEDD DOE/P/1	Under-Secretary, Head of Air, Noise and Wastes Directorate	47, 95, 100
Later: MR P CRITCHLEY	Under-Secretary, Head of Air, Noise and Wastes Directorate	279
Supported by: Dr F Feates	Member of Radioactive Waste Management Division (RWMD)	95, 100, 279
Dr A Duncan	Member, RWMD	95, 100

Witness Proof of Evidence	Qualifications & Position	Days of Appearance
MR B HOOKWAY 　DOE/P/2 Later:	MSc, MInstP; Senior Radiochemical Inspector	47
MR A WINDSOR	Superintending Radiochemical Inspector	279-280
Supported by: 　Dr F Feates	Member, RWMD	279-280

DTp WITNESS

MR R A O'SULLIVAN 　DTp/P/1	BSc, CChem, MRSC; Radiological Adviser to Secretary of State	56, 280
Supported by: 　Mr C Jones	Principal Engineer, Radioactive Materials Transport Division	280

MAFF WITNESSES

Witness Proof of Evidence	Qualifications & Position	Days of Appearance
MR P D CHAMBERLAIN 　MAFF/P/1	BSc, ARICS; Senior Surveyor	55
MR H R NEILSON 　MAFF/P/2 　Supported by:	Assistant Secretary, Fisheries Division	55, 276-277
Miss H K Dixon	Staff member, Fisheries Division	55
MR G F MEEKINGS 　MAFF/P/3	BSc, MInstP; Head of Atomic Energy Unit, Food Science Division	55, 276-277
DR N T MITCHELL 　MAFF/P/4	CChem, BSc, PhD, FRSC; Section Head, Directorate of Fisheries Research	55-56, 276-277, 279

NATIONAL RADIOLOGICAL PROTECTION BOARD (NRPB)
(Invited to appear at the Inquiry)

ADVOCATE

MR DAVID LATHAM, of Counsel

Instructed By:

TREASURY SOLICITOR

WITNESSES

Witness Proof of Evidence	Qualifications & Position	Days of Appearance
DR R H CLARKE NRPB/P/1	BSc, MSc, PhD; Board Secretary	99
SIR EDWARD POCHIN NRPB/P/2 Supported by:	DM, FRCP; Consultant to the Director	99, 151-154
Dr J A Reissland	PhD, MInstP; Physicist	151-154
Dr G N Kelly	BSc, PhD; Staff member, Assessment Department	151-154
Dr J A Dennis	Assistant Director (Physical Sciences)	151-154
Dr H Smith	Head of Biology Section	151-154
MR G A M WEBB NRPB/P/3	Assistant Director (Operations)	304

WITNESSES ON EMERGENCY PLANNING

Witness	Qualifications & Position	Days of Appearance
CEGB		
MR P T McINERNEY	CEng, MIEE, MIMechE, FBIM; Director of Production, South Eastern Region	266
MR R B PEPPER	BSc, MinstP; Principal Health Physicist	266
MR F E BENTLEY	BA, Dip in Radiological Protection; Health Physicist, Sizewell A Power Station	266
Local Planning Authorities (LPAs)		
MR J HANCOCK	Emergency Plans Officer, Suffolk County Council	266-268
MR D L BLAY	Chief Executive, Suffolk Coastal District Council	266-268
MR J M CRAIG	Deputy Chief Fire Officer, Suffolk Fire Service	266, 268-269
Suffolk Constabulary		
MR S MERRICKS	Assistant Chief Constable	266-267
MR R RUMSBY	Chief Superintendent	266-267
MR J ALLEN	Chief Inspector	266-267

Witness	Qualifications & Position	Days of Appearance
NII		
MR W S GRONOW	HM Deputy Chief Inspector of Nuclear Installations	266-268
MR B SWEENEY	HM Principal Inspector of Nuclear Installations	266, 268
DOE		
MR A WINDSOR	Superintending Radiochemical Inspector	266, 268
MR P BRAZENDALE	Principal Radiochemical Inspector	266, 268
MAFF		
MR T W NICOL	Chief Regional Officer (Eastern Region)	266, 268
MR G F MEEKINGS	BSc, MInstP; Head of Atomic Energy Unit	266, 268
MR R C GURD	Branch Head, Standards Division	266, 268
DR N T MITCHELL	CChem, BSc, PhD, FRSC; Section Head, Directorate of Fisheries Research	268
NRPB		
MR B HOLLIDAY	Head of Operational Protection Department	266-267
East Suffolk Health Authority		
DR M F H BUSH	District Medical Officer	266, 268
Anglian Water Authority		
MR B BLACKWELL	Safety and Emergency Planning Officer	266, 268
East Anglian Water Company		
MR K B CLARKE	General Manager and Chief Engineer	266, 268

NATIONAL CONSUMER BODY (became a statutory body with effect from
1 September 1983)

ELECTRICITY CONSUMERS' COUNCIL (ECC)

ADVOCATE

MR WILLIAM HICKS, of Counsel

Instructed By:

MRS C CARTER, Coward Chance, Solicitors

WITNESSES

Witness Proof of Evidence	Qualifications & Position	Days of Appearance
MR M BARNES ECC/P/1	MA; Chairman of the Council	98, 103-104

MR G S MACKERRON
  ECC/P/2
  ECC/P/6
  ECC/P/8
	BA, MA; Fellow of the Science
	Policy Research Unit (SPRU), Sussex
	University
		98-99, 110-111;
		102, 112;
		103, 115

MR S THOMAS
  ECC/P/3
  ECC/P/7
  ECC/P/8
	BSc; Research Fellow, SPRU, Sussex
	University
		99, 111-112;
		103, 112;
		115

MR I S JONES
  ECC/P/4
  ECC/P/5
  ECC/P/8
	MA; Research Officer, National
	Institute of Economic and Social
	Research
		102, 104, 113-115;
		103, 115;
		115

MEMBER OF PARLIAMENT

	Position	Days of Appearance
MR J S GUMMER	Member of Parliament for Eye, Suffolk, later for Suffolk Coastal	50, 300

OTHER PARTIES

ANTI-PWR CONSORTIUM OF TRADE UNIONS AND LOCAL AUTHORITIES (TULA)

ADVOCATE

MR A W FISHER

WITNESSES

Witness Proof of Evidence	Qualifications & Position	Days of Appearance

MR P J TAYLOR
  TULA/P/1
  TULA/P/2
and
	BA, DipSA; Director, Political
	Ecology Research Group Ltd (PERG)
		227-228
		228

MR R J KAYES TULA/P/2	BA, MSc, DipTP; Director, PERG	228

MR T SEGARS
  TULA/P/3
  TULA/P/5
Supported by:
  Mr D Mathews (P/3)
	National Executive Member, Fire
	Brigades Union (FBU)
	
	National Officer for Health and
	Safety, FBU
		270
		281
		
		270

MR R M POOLE
  TULA/P/4
  TULA/P/5
	Health Service National Officer,
	National Union of Public Employees
		270
		281

MR D MATHEWS TULA/P/5	National Officer for Health and Safety, FBU	281

MR J C ZERBIB
  TULA/P/6
 	
Supported by:
  Mr J Tassart
	Radiation protection engineer with
	Confederation Francaise Democratique
	de Travailleurs (CFDT)
	
	Nuclear safety specialist, CFDT
		297
		
		297

A POWER FOR GOOD LTD (APG)

ADVOCATE

MR G GREENHALGH

WITNESSES

Witness Proof of Evidence	Qualifications & Position	Days of Appearance
MR K R WILLIAMS APG/P/1	Head of Information Division of Public Affairs, Shell International Petroleum Co Ltd	Read to Inquiry on Day 52

Witness Proof of Evidence	Qualifications & Position	Days of Appearance
MR L G BROOKES APG/P/2	BA, DipEcon, FInstE; Economics consultant	52
MR M POTEMANS APG/P/3	Manager, Ebes MV (Belgian utility company)	54
DR L D HAMILTON APG/P/4	BA, BM, BCh, MA, DM, PhD, ABP; Head of Biomedical and Environmental Assessment Division, Brookhaven National Laboratory	54-55

BILLINGHAM AGAINST NUCLEAR DUMPING (BAND)

Witness	Qualifications & Position	Days of Appearance
MR R E N WILLIAMS BAND 01	CEng, FInstCE, HND; Consultant Engineer	303

CAMPAIGN FOR NUCLEAR DISARMAMENT (CND)

ADVOCATES

MR JOHN BOWYER, of Counsel
MR R P EDWARDS

Instructed By:

BINDMAN & PARTNERS, Solicitors

WITNESSES

Witness Proof of Evidence	Qualifications & Position	Days of Appearance
DR R V HESKETH CND/P/1	BSc, PhD, FInstP; Physicist, formerly employed in CEGB Research Department, Berkeley Nuclear Laboratories	283-285, 295
Supported by: Dr K W J Barnham	Nuclear Physicist, Blackett Laboratory, Imperial College, London	283-284, 295
MR D LOWRY CND/P/2	BSc; Member of Energy Research Group, Open University	284
MR R P EDWARDS CND/P/3	MA; Freelance journalist and researcher	284-285, 295

CENTRE FOR ENERGY STUDIES (CES)

ADVOCATE

MR C SWEET

WITNESSES

Witness Proof of Evidence	Qualifications & Position	Days of Appearance
MR C SWEET CES/P/1	BSc; Director of the CES and Senior Lecturer in Economics, South Bank Polytechnic	146
DR B FINE CES/P/2	BA, BPhil, PhD; Reader in Economics, Birkbeck College, University of London	147
DR R PAPADOPOULOS CES/P/3	MSc, PhD; Senior Lecturer and Fuel Technology Course Tutor, Chemical Engineering Department, South Bank Polytechnic	146
MR R L GILES CES/P/4	BSc, MA; Senior Lecturer in Econometrics, South Bank Polytechnic	147

COMMUNIST PARTY OF GREAT BRITAIN: EAST ANGLIAN DISTRICT COMMITTEE (CP:EADC)

Advocate & Witness	Qualifications & Position	Days of Appearance
MR S T SMITH CP:EADC 01	CEng, MIEE, AMIRTE; District Committee Member	143

COMMUNIST PARTY OF GREAT BRITAIN : LEISTON BRANCH (CP:LB)

Witness	Qualifications & Position	Days of Appearance
MR W HOWARD CP:LB 01	Branch Chairman; Leiston Town Councillor	294

COUNCIL FOR THE PROTECTION OF RURAL ENGLAND (CPRE)

ADVOCATE

MR JOHN TAYLOR, QC

Instructed By:

MR C J TIPPING, Knapp-Fishers, Solicitors

WITNESSES

Witness Proof of Evidence	Qualifications & Position	Days of Appearance
MR C KOMANOFF CPRE/P/1	Consultant in energy economics	82-83
MR R H JOHNSON CPRE/P/2	MA, Dip in Petroleum Economics; Director, Energy Resources Ltd	86-87, 89-92
DR M A BARRETT CPRE/P/3 Supported by:	BSc, PGCE, PhD; Member of Energy Research Group, Open University	86, 88-89
Dr H Miall	BA, PhD; Energy consultant, Earth Resources Research Ltd (ERRL)	86, 88-89
Dr F Nectoux	Researcher, ERRL	88-89
Mr D Baldock	BA, Dip in Population Growth Studies; Director, ERRL	88-89
DR B J CORY CPRE/P/4	BEng, DSc, FIEE; Reader in Electrical Engineering, Imperial College, London	84-86
MR B WILKINS CPRE/P/5	AEng; Senior Partner, Power Management Associates (Consultants)	91-92
DR F NECTOUX CPRE/P/6	Diplome d'Etudes Approfondies, Doctorate, Diploma of the Institute of Political Studies, Paris; Researcher, ERRL	93
MR C CONROY CPRE/P/7	BA; Consultant	93-94

THE ECOLOGY PARTY, THE WALES ECOLOGY PARTY, AND THE SCOTTISH ECOLOGY PARTY (JEP)

ADVOCATE

MR G E OUBRIDGE

WITNESSES

Witness Proof of Evidence	Qualifications & Position	Days of Appearance
MR G E OUBRIDGE JEP/P/1	Wales Ecology Party Representative on the UK Ecology Party Council	231-232
MR M GOLDSTICK JEP/P/2	BA, MA; Researcher	232
MR J GRAHAM JEP/P/3	Representative of the American Indian Movement Survival Group (AIMSG), Saskatchewan	232-233
MS A ALDRIDGE JEP/P/4 Supported by: Mr M Goldstick Mr J Graham	 BA, MA; Researcher Representative of AIMSG	233 233 233
MS L HENDRY JEP/P/5	MA; Scottish Representative on the UK Ecology Party Council	234
MS B FLICK JEP/P/6	Representative of the National Federation of Land Councils, Australia	233
MS J WINGFIELD (appearing on behalf of Mr J Tragenza) JEP/P/7	Representative of the Kokatha Peoples' Committee, and the Southern (Aboriginal) Land Council, South Australia	233

ERGONOMICS SOCIETY (ES)

ADVOCATE

MR JOHN RILEY, of Counsel

Instructed By:

RYLAND, MARTINEAU & CO, Solicitors

WITNESSES

Witness Proof of Evidence	Qualifications & Position	Days of Appearance
DR A R HALE ES/P/1	Senior Lecturer in Occupational Health and Safety, University of Aston in Birmingham	50, 223
DR L BAINBRIDGE ES/P/2	MA, MS, PhD; Reader in Psychology, University College, London	50, 223

Witness Proof of Evidence	Qualifications & Position	Days of Appearance
PROF K D DUNCAN ES/P/3	BA, PhD, FBPsS; Professor of Applied Psychology, UWIST	50, 223
DR D E EMBREY ES/P/4	Ergonomist, Human Reliability Associates Ltd	50, 223

All the above witnesses were supported by:

Mr D Whitfield	Senior Tutor in Applied Psychology and Head of the Ergonomics Development Unit, University of Aston in Birmingham	223

FRIENDS OF THE EARTH LTD (FOE)

ADVOCATE

MR JOHN HOWELL, of Counsel

Instructed By:

DENTON HALL & BURGIN, Solicitors

WITNESSES

Witness Proof of Evidence	Qualifications & Position	Days of Appearance
MR B KJELLSTROM FOE/P/1	Mechanical engineer; Head of Exergetics Energisystemteknik AB. (Formerly research engineer and manager at AB Atomenergi, the Swedish nuclear research establishment)	186-187
MR L HAHN FOE/P/2	Diplom; Leader of Projektgruppe Reaktorsicherheit, Oko-Institut (private research institute)	177-180
MR G C MINOR FOE/P/3	BS, MS; Vice-President, MHB Technical Associates (formerly Manager in the field of control system design and development, General Electric Company)	179-180
MR C H GREEN FOE/P/4	BA, BArch, MArch; Research Fellow, Flood Hazard Research Centre, Middlesex Polytechnic	181
MR W C PATTERSON FOE/P/5	BSc, MSc; Consultant and writer	182

GREATER LONDON COUNCIL (GLC)

ADVOCATE

MR WILLIAM BIRTLES, of Counsel

Instructed By:

GLC LEGAL BRANCH

WITNESSES

Witness Proof of Evidence	Qualifications & Position	Days of Appearance
MR D W HUTCHINSON GLC/P/1	MRIBA, MRTPI, DipArch, DipTP; Principal Development Planner, Transportation and Development Department	126-127
MR J A MACADAM GLC/P/2	BSc, MSc, MInstE; Head of CHP section, Orchard Partners (consultants)	138-140
MR S HODGKINSON GLC/P/3	BSc, MPhil, Dip in Housing & Energy Studies; Researcher, Earth Resources Research Ltd (ERRL)	128, 137- 138, 140
and MR C MOORCRAFT GLC/P/3	AADip; Energy consultant	140
DR F NECTOUX GLC/P/4	Diplome d'Etudes Approfondies, Doctorate, Diploma of the Institute of Political Studies, Paris; Researcher, ERRL	128
DR N C MASON GLC/P/5 Supported by:	BA, MA, PhD; Research Officer, GLC Economic Policy Group	127-128
Mr A Atkinson	AADip, MArch & Urban Planning; Consultant, Orchard Partners	127-128
DR D SLATER GLC/P/6 GLC/P/7 Supported by:	BSc, PhD, CEng, CChem, FRSC, FInstE, FInstPet; Executive Director, Technica Ltd	216-217 254-255
Dr R A Cox	MA, PhD, CEng, FRMetS, MInstE; Executive Director, Technica Ltd	216-217
Dr P J Kayes	BSc, PhD, CEng, FRSH, MInstGasE, MInstCombu.; Principal Staff Engineer, Technica Ltd	216-217, 254-255
Dr R F Griffiths	BSc, PhD, DSc, FRMetS, MInstP; Assistant Director, Pollution Research Unit, UMIST	216-217, 254-255
Dr J G A Croll	Reader in Structural Engineering, University College, London (UCL)	216-217
Dr G N Kelly	BSc, PhD; Staff Member, NRPB Assessment Department	216-217, 254-255
Ms B Morgan	BSc, CEng, ARSM; Senior Materials Engineer, Technica Ltd	254-255

Witness Proof of Evidence	Qualifications & Position	Days of Appearance
DR J G A CROLL GLC/P/8	BEng, PhD, CEng, MIStructE; Reader in Structural Engineering, UCL	255-256
AIR COMM. G INNES, CBE GLC/P/9 Supported by: Mr L G Wisbey	FBIM; Head of Emergency Planning Division Deputy Head of Emergency Planning Division	217 217
MR K A BUCHAN GLC/P/10 Supported by: Mr S J Bagnall	MA, MSc; Group Planner, Transportation and Development Department HNC; Technical Officer, Transportation and Development Department	281 281
MR L E PETERKEN GLC/P/11	MA; Controller of Operational Services	282

IPSWICH BOROUGH COUNCIL, CAMBRIDGE CITY COUNCIL AND NORWICH CITY COUNCIL (IBC)

Witness Proof of Evidence	Qualifications & Position	Days of Appearance
COUNCILLOR J C CANN IBC/P/1	Member of Ipswich Borough Council	300

IPSWICH FRIENDS OF THE EARTH (IDF)

Witness Proof of Evidence	Qualifications & Position	Days of Appearance
MR R SADLER IDF/P/1 Supported by: Ms L Spencer	MA; Partner of New Perspectives (research consultancy) MA; Partner of New Perspectives	301 301

THE JOINT LOCAL PARISH COUNCILS (JPCs)

ADVOCATE

MR R A STRAND, OBE

WITNESSES

Witness Proof of Evidence	Qualifications & Position	Days of Appearance
PROF M W THRING JPC/P/1	ScD, FEng, FIMechE, FIEE, FIChemE, FInstP; Professor (Emeritus) of Mechanical Engineering, Queen Mary College, London	188
MR C FLAVIN JPC/P/2	Senior Researcher, Worldwatch Institute	240
PROF D J ZEIGLER JPC/P/3	BSc, MA, PhD; Assistant Professor and Director of Geography, Old Dominion University, Norfolk, Virginia, USA	295-296
MAYOR S R REED JPC/P/4 Supported by: Mr D H Konkle	Mayor and Chief Executive Officer, Harrisburg, Pennsylvania, USA Fire Chief and Emergency Management Director, Harrisburg	296 296
MR R D SINGLETON JPC/P/5	BSc, CEng, MICE, MIHT; Partner, Denis Wilson and Partners (Consulting Engineers and Transportation Planners)	302

LEISTON TOWN COUNCIL (LTC)

Witness	Qualifications & Position	Days of Appearance
MR R L MORRIS LTC 01	Town Clerk	300

NATIONAL COAL BOARD (NCB)

ADVOCATES

MR PETER GOLDSMITH, of Counsel
MR JEREMY BURFORD, of Counsel

Instructed By:

NCB LEGAL DEPARTMENT

WITNESSES

Witness Proof of Evidence	Qualification & Position	Days of Appearance
MR M J PARKER NCB/P/1 Supported by: Mr R Ormerod	MA; Director of Central Planning CEng, MSc; Staff member, Department of Central Planning	56, 141-142 141-142

NATIONAL UNION OF MINEWORKERS (NUM)

ADVOCATES

MR A SCARGILL, Union President
MR P J TAYLOR
DR M McCARTHY

WITNESSES

Witness Proof of Evidence	Qualifications & Position	Days of Appearance
DR G GUDGIN NUM/P/1	BA, PhD; Senior Research Officer, University of Cambridge Department of Applied Economics; member of the Cambridge Economic Policy Group	148-149
and MR S FOTHERGILL NUM/P/1	BA; Research Associate, University of Cambridge Department of Land Economy	148-149
THE RT HON A W BENN, MP NUM/P/2	Formerly Minister of Technology, Minister of Power, Secretary of State for Industry and Secretary of State for Energy	150
DR R MOURE NUM/P/3	BSc, MSc, PhD; Industrial Hygienist, United Automobile Workers of America	260-261
MR P J TAYLOR NUM/P/4 and	BA, DipSA; Director, Political Ecology Research Group Ltd (PERG)	261
MR R J KAYES NUM/P/4	BA, MSc, DipTP; Director, PERG	261

NORFOLK COUNTY LABOUR PARTY (NCLP)

Advocate & Witness Proof of Evidence	Qualifications & Position	Days of Appearance
MR R G ROUND NCLP/P/1 NCLP/P/2	CEng, FIEE; Formerly Deputy Chief Engineer, Eastern Electricity Board	146 224

NORTHUMBERLAND COUNTY COUNCIL (NCC)

ADVOCATE

MR DUNCAN OUSELEY, of Counsel

Instructed By:

Mr P J BRADY, Solicitor

No witnesses were called on behalf of NCC

NORTHUMBERLAND AND NEWCASTLE SOCIETY (N&NSoc)

Witness Proof of Evidence	Qualifications & Position	Days of Appearance
MR D WILBIE-CHALK N&NSoc/P/1	MA, DipArch, ARIBA; Former County Chairman of N&NSoc	101

PORTSKEWETT ACTION GROUP (PAG)

Advocate & Witness Proof of Evidence	Qualifications & Position	Days of Appearance
MR G H HANCOCK PAG/P/1	Chairman of the Group	269

PRO NUCLEAR POWER PEOPLE (PNPP)

Witness	Qualifications & Position	Days of Appearance
MR D STANLEY PNPP 01	Local resident	49

RIDGEWAY CONSULTANTS (KL)

ADVOCATE

DR K LITTLE

WITNESSES

Witness Proof of Evidence	Qualifications & Position	Days of Appearance
DR K LITTLE KL/P/1 KL/P/4	MA, BSc, DPhil; Consultant	51 50-51
MR A S PLANE KL/P/2	BME; Consultant	50
MR H G WARD KL/P/5	Former journalist	51

ROPE AND ROPE LTD (ROPE)

Witness Proof of Evidence	Qualifications & Position	Days of Appearance
MR R G A ROPE ROPE/P/1	BA; Owner and occupier of land in the Sizewell area (former member of Leiston Urban District Council and representative on the Area Planning Committee)	289

R ROSENTHAL AND OTHERS (RR)

ADVOCATE

MR R ROSENTHAL

WITNESSES

Witness Proof of Evidence	Qualifications & Position	Days of Appearance
MR R ROSENTHAL RR/P/1	BA; Post-graduate student	231
MR A PICKERING RR/P/2	Former Personnel Officer at the Rossing Mine, Namibia	231
MR S PICCIOTTO RR/P/3	BA; Senior Lecturer in Law, University of Warwick	231

ROYAL INSTITUTE OF BRITISH ARCHITECTS, EASTERN REGION (RIBA:ER)

Advocate & Witness Proof of Evidence	Qualifications & Position	Days of Appearance
MR J CARTER RIBA:ER/P/1	ARIBA, ARAIA, DipCons; Registered architect	208

SOUTH AND WEST YORKSHIRE, NOTTINGHAMSHIRE AND DERBYSHIRE COUNTY COUNCILS (YND)

ADVOCATE

MR H S HOARE, Solicitor

Witness Proof of Evidence	Qualifications & Position	Days of Appearance
COUNTY COUNCILLOR K PATTERSON YND/P/1	MA, PhD; Chairman of Traffic and Highways Committee, West Yorkshire County Council	144

STOP SIZEWELL B ASSOCIATION AND ECOROPA (SSBA)

ADVOCATES

MR G SEARLE
MR J VALENTINE

WITNESSES

Witness Proof of Evidence	Qualifications & Position	Days of Appearance

PROF J W JEFFERY
  SSBA/P/1
  SSBA/P/4
	BA, PhD; Emeritus Professor of
	Crystallography, University of London
		149-150
		243-244

MR P P BUNYARD
  SSBA/P/2
  SSBA/P/11
	BA, MA; Editor of 'The Ecologist' and
	consultant editor for the United Nations
	Environment Programme
		189-190
		299

DR R MARSHALL SSBA/P/3	DPhil; Lecturer in Physics, University of Keele	145
PROF R E BLACKITH SSBA/P/5	BSc, PhD, DSc, FInstS; Associate Professor of Zoology, Trinity College, Dublin	257-258

Witness Proof of Evidence	Qualifications & Position	Days of Appearance
DR M STUART SSBA/P/6	BSc, MSc, PhD, FInstS; Senior Lecturer in Statistics, Trinity College, Dublin	258
DR A M STEWART SSBA/P/7	DMed, FRCP; Senior Research Fellow, Birmingham University	297-298
DR R BERTELL SSBA/P/8	BA, MA, PhD; Research consultant	259-260
MRS J L PICKETT SSBA/P/9	Part-time Youth Worker, Leiston Youth Club	299-300
MS L CHADWICK SSBA/P/10	BA; Writer; resident of Leiston	298-299
DR F BARNABY SSBA/P/12	PhD; Visiting Professor of Peace Studies, Free University of Amsterdam, Director of the World Disarmament Campaign and Co-Director of Just Defence	305

SUFFOLK PRESERVATION SOCIETY (SPS)

ADVOCATE

MR J POPHAM, FRICS; Director of the Society

WITNESSES

Witness Proof of Evidence	Qualifications & Position	Days of Appearance
MR R G BLYTHE SPS/P/1	FRSL; Writer	293
PROF H MOGGRIDGE SPS/P/2	AILA, ARIBA, AADip; Senior Partner, Colvin and Moggridge; Professor of Landscape Architecture, Sheffield University	289
DR R E RANDALL SPS/P/3	MA, MSc, PhD; Teacher and researcher	294
MR C E RANSON SPS/P/4	BSc; Formerly Deputy Regional Officer for East Anglia, Nature Conservancy Council	294
MR R G ROUND SPS/P/5	CEng, FIEE; Formerly Deputy Chief Engineer, Eastern Electricity Board	250
MR G B PARKER SPS/P/6	MA, MScCE, MInstCE, MIHT, MRTPI, MCIT; Consultant	293

TOWN AND COUNTRY PLANNING ASSOCIATION (TCPA)

ADVOCATES

MR J BLAKE, Executive Committee Vice Chairman
MS J ARMSTRONG

WITNESSES

Witness Proof of Evidence	Qualifications & Position	Days of Appearance
PROF P R ODELL TCPA/P/1	Professor of International Energy Studies and Director of the Centre for International Energy Studies (EURICES), Erasmus University, Rotterdam	129-130
MR R P STEENBLIK TCPA/P/2	BSc; Researcher, EURICES	129, 132
MR M PRIOR TCPA/P/3	BSc, MSc, MA; Consultant	132, 185-186
MR S CROWTHER TCPA/P/4	Senior Lecturer in Industrial Relations, Sunderland Polytechnic	135
MR M INCE TCPA/P/5	BSc; Associate Editor of 'Technology' magazine	131
MR C SWEET TCPA/P/6	BSc; Director of the Centre for Energy Studies and Senior Lecturer in Economics, South Bank Polytechnic	133, 135
DR G THOMPSON TCPA/P/7 Supported by: Mr S Sholly	BSc, BME, PhD; Consulting scientist to the Union of Concerned Scientists, USA BSc; Technical Research Associate with the Union of Concerned Scientists, USA	203, 205-206 205-206
DR M RESNIKOFF TCPA/P/8	PhD; Staff Scientist and Co-Director, Sierra Club Radioactive Waste Campaign, USA	209-210
MR R F FORDHAM TCPA/P/9	BSc; Formerly Principal Professional and Technology Officer, UKAEA Safety and Reliability Directorate	203, 207

WANSBECK DISTRICT COUNCIL (WDC)

ADVOCATE

MR R R GREY, Solicitor

No witnesses were called on behalf of WDC

THE WEIR GROUP PLC (WG)

Witness Proof of Evidence	Qualifications & Position	Days of Appearance
LORD WEIR WG/P/1	Chairman of the Company	185

WELSH ANTI NUCLEAR ALLIANCE (WANA)

ADVOCATE

MR H W RICHARDS

WITNESSES

Witness Proof of Evidence	Qualifications & Position	Days of Appearance
MR P M ROWNTREE WANA/P/1	BA; Member of the Policy Research Unit, South Yorkshire County Council; Director, Nuclear Information and Research Institute	144
MR H W RICHARDS WANA/P/2	BArch, MA, MRTPI; Local government planner	144-145

INDIVIDUALS

i) Individuals who gave evidence which was offered for cross-examination

Witness Proof of Evidence	Qualifications & Position	Days of Appearance
DR A E M ASH AA/P/1	LCRP, MRCS, MA; Doctor	230
MR F BARKER FB 01	Member of Planning and Highways Committee, Suffolk County Council, and Member of Leiston Town Council	288
LORD BOWDEN OF CHESTERFIELD VB 01	MA, PhD, MScTech, DS, LL.D, CEng, FIEEE, FIEE, FICE; Formerly Dean of the Faculty of Technology, Manchester University, Principal of UMIST and Minister of State of the Department of Education and Science	105

Witness Proof of Evidence	Qualifications & Position	Days of Appearance
REV D J DRYE DJD 01	BSc; Cleric	226
DR A E HARDMAN AEH/P/1	MBBS, MRCPsych, DPM; Psychiatrist	300
MR R G HARE WS/R/94	Local farmer	301
MR N JENKINS NJ/P/1	Technical journalist	301
MR E H LANGLEY EHL/P/1	Resident of Leiston	108
MR M I MICHAELS MIM/P/1	Formerly Head of Atomic Energy Division, Department of Energy	49
MS N M PILKINGTON NMP/P/1	BEd	226
MS M B POWELL MBP/P/1	BA	294
MR D ROSS DR/P/1	Journalist	101
MR R STERNE RFS 01		Read by Mr W Jones on Day 281
MR G B STONER GS/P/1	BSc	101
DR J B THRING JBT/P/1	BArch, MCD, PhD, MRTPI; Consultant	102
MS A WILKS AW/P/1		101
PROF E M WILSON EMW/P/1	BSc, MSc, PhD, FICE, FASCE; Professor of Hydraulic Engineering and Chairman of the Department of Civil Engineering, University of Salford	142

ii)   Individuals who made statements to the Inquiry

Witness	Qualifications & Position	Days of Appearance
MRS E S CHAPMAN ESC 01	Resident of Leiston	288
MRS J FOSTER JF 01		288
MRS W JOLMES WH 01	Resident of Leiston	294
MS H MURRELL HM 01	MA	Read by Mr R Green on Day 258
MS D OLIVER DO 01	Resident of Leiston	289
MR R F STEARN STN 01	Local farmer	306
MS H M WILSON HW 01		306

WITNESSES CALLED BY THE INQUIRY

NATURE CONSERVANCY COUNCIL (NAT)

Witness Proof of Evidence	Qualifications & Position	Days of Appearance
MR C J D SHACKLES NAT/P/1	BSc, MIBiol; Assistant Regional Officer for East Suffolk	291

SOUTH OF SCOTLAND ELECTRICITY BOARD (SSEB)

ADVOCATE

MR BRUCE WEIR, QC (Now Mr Justice Weir)

Instructed By:

MR D A S MacLAREN, Board Secretary

WITNESSES

Witness Proof of Evidence	Qualifications & Position	Days of Appearance
MR D J MILLER SSEB/P/1-3 Supported by:	BSc, FEng, FIMechE, FIEE; Chairman	241-242
Dr A F Pexton	BSc, PhD, FIMechE, FIEE; Director of Engineering	241-242

INDIVIDUALS

Witness Proof of Evidence	Qualifications & Position	Days of Appearance
DR M F H BUSH MFB/P/1	MB, BS, FFCM, DPM, DCH; District Medical Officer, East Suffolk Health Authority	193
SIR ALISTAIR FRAME AGF/P/1	MA, BSc, FIMechE, FEng; Deputy Chairman and Chief Executive, Rio Tinto-Zinc Corporation PLC	109, 134
MR D C ION ION/P/1	MA, MIGeol, FGS, FInstPet, FRSA; Energy resources analyst and consultant	245-246
PROF T A KLETZ TAK/P/1	BSc, FEng, FRSC, FIChemE; Senior Research Fellow, Department of Chemical Engineering, Loughborough University (formerly safety adviser to ICI Petrochemicals Division)	229-230
PROF J WILLIAMSON JW/P/1	Senior Fellow, Institute for International Economics, Washington DC	225

COUNSEL TO THE INQUIRY

MR HENRY BROOKE, QC
MR ANDRZEJ KOLODZIEJ, of Counsel

Instructed By:

TREASURY SOLICITOR

LETTERS OF OBJECTION AND WRITTEN REPRESENTATIONS

Over 4000 letters of objection and written representations were received by the Inquiry. All were taken into account.

A number of letters of objection from the individuals or groups listed below, were read out at the Inquiry on Days 52,75,87,109 and 143 to give an indication of the points most frequently made:

Abbott, E F
Aberystwyth Anti-Nuclear
 Group
Armitage, P H
Armstrong, J
Barker, D W S, P P & R
Bateson, J
Bedfordshire County Council
Blensdorf, O
Borrett, J
Brook, M
Call, J C
Cambridge Anti-Nuclear
 Campaign
Carver, B
Clements, V R et al
Coates, J P
Cocker, W E
Coles, M
Crawford, M
Darch, M P
Davey, T
Dixon, M
Dodd, G T
Dow, P
East Anglian Landscape
 Association
Ecology Party in Wales
Elliott, N
Evans, G D
Evans, P
Finney, Dr D
Foster, B J
Garrett, T
Gilfedder, K & E
Gillys, A R
Hackney Anti-Nuclear Group
Hardcastle, D J A
Hayes, M R

Hook, Dr D
Hooper, Dr G
Horan, P
Horwood, M J
Laycock, S
London Borough of Hackney
Long, S J
Lowry, D (Energy Research Group,
 Open University)
Macdowell, M
Macfarlane, J M
Marjoram, J
Matheson, A
Mathew, D E
Mills, J
Murray, J E
Nation, C
North West Leicestershire District
 Council
Parr, F
Phillips, M H
Quorn, P
Redfern, R
Richards, H
Rope & Rope Ltd
Sander, M
Skirrow, P J
Somervell, D
Suffolk Association of Local
 Councils
Sweetman, W T C
Tilley, P
Turner, A
Wade, A F
Welbourne, J E
West, S L
Westgate, R
White, R
Wills, S & N

In addition, reference was made to written representations from the following:

Ackroyd, Prof P R & E A
(Days 300, 303, 334)
Adams, J (Days 229, 319)
Babcock Power Limited (Days 131,
185, 241, 290, 309, 322)
Bedfordshire County Council
(Day 251)
British Electrical and Allied
Manufacturers' Association
Limited (Days 47, 131, 309, 322, 329)
British Nuclear Forum (Days 47,
131, 309, 314, 322, 329)
British Nuclear Fuels plc: Staff
Side (Day 308)
Burgoyne, Rev P J (Days 303, 334)
Burns, W D & W V (Day 334)
Butterworth, R (Day 304)
Chadwick, L et al (Days 297-299),
306, 319, 334)
Chemical Industries Association
(Days 308, 322)
City of Newcastle Upon Tyne (Day 46)
Cliff, E B C (Day 308)
Confederation of British Industry
(Days 47, 308)
Cooper, D (Day 280)
Countryside Commission (Days 287, 306
334)
Dombey, Dr N (Day 306)
Eastern Regional Council of the Labour
Party (Days 152, 298, 331, 335)
Edwards, G E (Day 308)
Electricity Consumers' Council
(Day 225)
Electricity Supply Industry
Employees' National Committee
(Days 152-153, 155, 157, 217, 308-309,
312, 318, 331, 335)
Farnes, N R (Days 292-293)
Flatman, K (Day 288)
Fremlin, Prof J H (Days 298, 304, 308)
General, Municipal, Boilermakers &
Allied Trades Union (Days 217, 308
318, 320, 331, 335)
Gimson, R A S (Day 312)
Hammick, V (Day 308)

Hare, R G (Days 293, 301-303, 313,
334)
Henney, A (Chairman, London
Electricity Consultative Council)
(Days 111, 125, 240)
Hill, M H (Day 263)
Institution of Professional Civil
Servants (Days 282, 320)
James, J M (Day 306)
Joint Parish Councils (Days 302-
303, 334)
Keeble, E (Days 293, 334)
Leather, V M (Day 306)
London Area Ecology Party
(Days 251, 333)
Marin, A (London School of
Economics) (Days 243, 278, 321)
330)
Morgan, G R (Day 305)
Nature Conservancy Council
(Days 291, 334)
Newland, D N (Day 334)
Ogilvie, G S (Days 286-287, 289,
334)
Proctor, K H, MP (Days 278, 308)
Quance, S (Day 308)
Scottish Campaign to Resist the
Atomic Menace (Day 100)
Shepherd, G T (Days 322, 330)
Shurman, L P (Day 287)
Socialist Environment and Resources
Association (Day 313)
Spencer, Sir K (Days 266, 278, 308)
Staffordshire County Council
(Day 309)
Thring, Prof M W (Day 145)
Trades Union Congress (Day 188)
Transport & General Workers' Union
(Days 308-309, 331)
UKAEA Whitley Council (Staff Side)
(Day 308)
Uranium Institute (Days 133, 135,
308)
Westleton Parish Council (Day 287)
Worster, N G (Day 308)

ALPHABETICAL LIST OF STATEMENTS OF CASE,

PROOFS OF EVIDENCE AND ADDENDA

This list contains all the statements of case, proofs of
evidence and related addenda. It does not include
supporting documents or written representations. The number
on the right hand side of each entry is the Inquiry
reference number. This shows the party submitting the
document and whether the document is a statement of case
(denoted by 01) or a proof of evidence (denoted by P and the
number of the proof).

ANTI PWR CONSORTIUM OF TRADE UNIONS AND LOCAL AUTHORITIES   TULA 01
    Statement of Case. December 1983. 12pp

  TAYLOR, P.   TULA/P/1
    The effects of a severe reactor accident at the proposed Sizewell B
    Station upon agriculture and fisheries in the UK and neighbouring
    countries. May 1984. 18pp.

  TAYLOR, P. AND KAYES, R.   TULA/P/2
    Consequences of severe accidents both to PWR's and in the
    transportation of spent fuel and the adequacy of the emergency planning
    arrangements. May 1984. 34pp.

  SEGARS, T.   TULA/P/3
    Evidence of the Fire Brigades Union on emergency planning arrangements
    for reactor accidents. July 1984. 12pp.

  POOLE, R.   TULA/P/4
    Evidence of the National Union of Public Employees on emergency planning
    arrangements for reactor accidents. July 1984. 13pp; appendix.

  MATHEWS, D. et al.   TULA/P/5
    Evidence of Fire Brigades Union and National Union of Public Employees on
    transportation of irradiated fuel. September 1984. 5pp.

  ZERBIB, J. C.   TULA/P/6
    Dosimetric performances of different groups of Light Water Reactors.
    September 1984. 36pp, inc. tables. (1 Addendum).

A POWER FOR GOOD   APG 01
    Statement of Case. March 1983. 12pp. (1 Addendum).

  WILLIAMS, K.   APG/P/1
    The Need for Nuclear Power. March 1983. 6pp; 1 fig. (1 Addendum).

  BROOKES, L. G.   APG/P/2
    Need for a significant nuclear programme in the United Kingdom and the
    relative roles of energy conservation and new energy supply. March 1983.
    27pp. (1 Addendum).

  POTEMANS, M.   APG/P/3
    Why nuclear energy in Belgium? March 1983. 24pp. (2 Addenda).

  HAMILTON, L. D.   APG/P/4
    The health effects of the coal and nuclear fuel cycles. March 1983.
    27pp. inc. figures. (1 Addendum).

ASH, A.   AA/P/1
    Proof of evidence. May 1984. 2pp.

BARKER, F.   FB 01
    Statement . October 1984. 3pp.

BILLINGHAM AGAINST NUCLEAR DUMPING   BAND 01
    Evidence to the Sizewell B Public Inquiry. December 1984. 42pp.
    (1 Addendum).

BINNIE AND PARTNERS
  BAKER, A. C. J.   BIN/P/1
  The Severn Barrage. September 1984. 5pp.

BOWDEN, LORD   VB 01
  CANDU - An alternative policy for this country. 1982. 34pp.

  BOWDEN, LORD   VB 01 (REV)
  The case for CANDU. May 1983. (Various pagings). (5 Addenda).

BRITISH NUCLEAR FUELS   BNFL 01
    Statement of Case. 1982. 11pp.

  AVERY, D. G.   BNFL/P/1
  Concerning the nuclear fuel cycle. 1982. 55pp; separate vol. of
  appendices. (12 Addenda).

BUSH, M. F. H.   MFB/P/1
  Leukaemia in East Suffolk. East Suffolk Health Authority.
  September 1983. 11pp; appendices. (2 Addenda).

CAMPAIGN FOR NUCLEAR DISARMAMENT   CND 01
    Statement of Case. CND Sizewell Working Group. September 1983. 3pp.

  HESKETH, R. V.   CND/P/1
  Nuclear power UK, nuclear weapons USA. September 1984. 117pp.
  (2 Addenda).

  LOWRY, D.   CND/P/2
  Safeguarding the future? September 1984. 74pp. (1 Addendum).

  EDWARDS, R.   CND/P/3
  Proof of evidence on behalf of CND. October 1984. 15pp. (2 Addenda).

CENTRAL ELECTRICITY GENERATING BOARD   **CEGB 01**
    Statement of Case. 1982. 7 vols.
    Vol.1 - pages 1-62   CEGB 01/A
    Vol.2 - pages 63-197   CEGB 01/B
    Appendices A-G   CEGB 01/C
    Appendix H   CEGB 01/D
    Appendix J   CEGB 01/E
    Appendix L   CEGB 01/F
    Appendix M   CEGB 01/G

  CENTRAL ELECTRICITY GENERATING BOARD   CEGB 01/E (REV)
  Annex to the CEGB Statement of Case (Appendix J - Revised): A
  description of the Sizewell B PWR Reference Design. CEGB.
  December 1983. 40pp; figures.

CENTRAL ELECTRICITY GENERATING BOARD   CEGB 02
   Sizewell B PWR Pre-Construction Safety Report. 1982. 13 vols.
   Vol.1 : Chap 1 - Introduction, general description of station   CEGB 02/A
                      site and surroundings.
          : Chap 2 - Strategy for ensuring nuclear safety.
          : Chap 3 - General design aspects of system and plant.
   Vol.2 : Chap 4 - Reactor   CEGB 02/B
          : Chap 5(part) - Reactor coolant system and connected systems.
   Vol.3 : Chap 5(cont)   CEGB 02/C
   Vol.4 : Chap 6 - Engineered safety systems.   CEGB 02/D
          : Chap 7 - Control and instrumentation.
   Vol.5 : Chap 8 - Main and essential electrical systems.   CEGB 02/E
          : Chap 9 - Auxiliary systems.
   Vol.6 : Chap 10 - Steam and power conversion system.   CEGB 02/F
          : Chap 11 - Radioactive waste management.
   Vol.7 : Chap 12 - Radiological protection.   CEGB 02/G
          : Chap 13 - The fuel storage and handling systems.
   Vol.8 : Chap 14 - Civil works and structures.   CEGB 02/H
   Vol.9 : Chap 15(part) - Fault analysis.   CEGB 02/I
   Vol.10 : Chap 15(cont)   CEGB 02/J
   Vol.11 : Chap 15(cont)   CEGB 02/K
   Vol.12 : Chap 15(cont)   CEGB 02/L
   Vol.13 : Chap 15(cont)   CEGB 02/M
            Chap 16 - Decommissioning

CENTRAL ELECTRICITY GENERATING BOARD   CEGB 03
   Sizewell B PWR Reference Design. April 1982. NNC. 4 vols.
   Vol.1 : (Chaps 1-5 of PCSR)   CEGB 03/A
   Vol.2 : (Chaps 6-9 of PCSR)   CEGB 03/B
   Vol.3 : (Chaps 10-14 of PCSR)   CEGB 03/C
   Vol.4 : Drawings   CEGB 03/D

BAKER, J. W.   CEGB/P/1
   CEGB Policy. 1982. 76pp. (13 Addenda).

MATTHEWS, R. R.   CEGB/P/2
   CEGB approach to nuclear safety. 1982. 84pp. (2 Addenda).

WRIGHT, J. K.   CEGB/P/3
   Alternative methods of electricity generation. 1982. 103pp, inc.
   appendices. (7 Addenda).

JENKIN, F. P.   CEGB/P/4
   The need for Sizewell B. 1982. 155pp, inc. appendices. (24 Addenda).

DAVIES, C. H.   CEGB/P/5
   Scenarios and electricity demand. 1982. 122pp; appendix.
   (13 Addenda).

HUGHES, P. R.   CEGB/P/6
   Fossil fuel supplies. 1982. 144pp; inc. appendices. (15 Addenda).

TOWNSEND, M.   CEGB/P/7
   Uranium supplies. 1982. 37pp, inc. appendices. (2 Addenda).

WILSON, A.
Construction time, cost and operating performances of PWR, AGR, and
Coal-fired generating plant. 1982. 4 vols. (12 Addenda).
Vol 1. 84pp

CEGB/P/8

CEGB/P/8A

Vol 2. Diagrams, tables and appendices. (Various pagings).
Vol 3. Appendix 5: NNC target construction programme.
     By: McFarlane, J. D. 21pp; figures.
Vol 4. Appendix C: NNC cost estimate for Sizewell 'B'.
     By: Flint, R. A. 1983. 32pp; including annex.

CEGB/P/8B
CEGB/P/8C

CEGB/P/8D

WRIGHT, J. K.
The nuclear fuel cycle. 1982. 39pp; appendices. (8 Addenda).

CEGB/P/9

GEORGE, B. V.
Design of Sizewell 'B' PWR. 1982. 237pp. (17 Addenda).

CEGB/P/10

HARRISON, J. R.
The safety case. 1982. 154pp, inc. appendices. (16 Addenda).

CEGB/P/11

EDMONDSON, B.
Pressure circuit component integrity. 1982. 170pp, inc. appendices.
(10 Addenda).

CEGB/P/12

WHITTLE, M. J.
Non-destructive testing. 1982. 96pp, inc. appendices; tables; figures.
(5 Addenda).

CEGB/P/13

SMEDLEY, G. P.
Independent Inspection Agency. 1982. 22pp, inc. appendix.

CEGB/P/14

NEWELL, J. E.
Steam generator tube integrity. 1982. 76pp. (4 Addenda).

CEGB/P/15

GITTUS, J. H
Degraded Core Analysis. 1982. 2 vols. (7 Addenda).
Vol 1. 83pp
Vol 2. figs, tables, appendices

CEGB/P/16

CEGB/P/16A
CEGB/P/16B

BONNELL, J. A.
Biological effects of radiation and medical supervision of radiation
workers. 1982. 45pp, inc. appendices. (4 Addenda).

CEGB/P/17

PEPPER, R. B.
Radiological protection in normal operation. 1982. 61pp.
inc. appendices; map. (4 Addenda).

CEGB/P/18

McINERNEY, P. T.
Commissioning, operation maintenance and operator training. 1982.
76pp; inc. appendix. (4 Addenda).

CEGB/P/19

PASSANT, F. H.
Radioactive waste management. 1982. 101pp, inc. appendices.
(2 Addenda).

CEGB/P/20

FLOWERS, R.
The disposal of low level and intermediate level solid wastes.
1982. 45pp. (5 Addenda).

CEGB/P/21

WOMACK, G. J.   CEGB/P/22
  Transport of irradiated fuel. 1982. 117pp, inc. appendices.
  (8 Addenda).

SINGLETON, L   CEGB/P/23
  The transport of irradiated fuel by rail. 1982. 118pp, inc.
  appendices. (5 Addenda).

GREGORY, A. R.   CEGB/P/24
  Decommissioning. 1982. 24pp. (4 Addenda).

GAMMON, K. M.   CEGB/P/25
  Site selection and site specific aspects. 1982. 27pp. (6 Addenda).

ARNOLD, P. J.   CEGB/P/27
  Systems benefits of the PWR development at Sizewell and transmission
  connections. 1982. 16pp. (8 Addenda).

MAWER, W. T.   CEGB/P/28
  The cooling water system. 1982. 14pp.

HAWES, F. B.   CEGB/P/29
  Ecological consequences of the use of cooling water. 1982. 25pp,
  inc. appendix.

HENDERSON, B.   CEGB/P/30A
  Architecture. 1982. 8pp. (1 Addendum).

YOUNGMAN, P.   CEGB/P/31A
  Landscape. 1982. 8pp. (2 Addenda).

HENDERSON AND YOUNGMAN   CEGB/P/30 and CEGB/P/31B
  Figures.

DUTTON, L. M. C.   CEGB/P/32
  The reduction of doses to operators. 1982. 42pp; figures.
  (2 Addenda).

DUTTON, L. M. C.   CEGB/P/33
  Radiological releases from design basis accidents. 1982. 66pp.
  (3 Addenda).

FARMER, P. R.   CEGB/P/34
  Code validation for loss of coolant accidents. 1982. 25pp; figures.
  (4 Addenda).

HEALEY, T and BOARD, S   CEGB/P/37
  Fuel clad ballooning. 1982. 29pp; table, figures. (4 Addenda).

ANDERSON, D. W.   CEGB/P/39
  Fuel management in the PWR. 1982. 27pp.

WARD, D. A.   CEGB/P/43
  Loss of coolant accidents (LOCA). 1982. 56pp; figures. (2 Addenda).

VIGNES, A.   CEGB/P/44
  Reactor Pressure Vessel Manufacture. 1983. 191pp; inc. appendices.
  (1 Addendum).

HARRISON, J. R.   CEGB/P/45
  Health and Safety. Department Assessment. February 1983. 49pp;
  inc. appendix. (2 Addenda).

BAKER, J. W.   CEGB/P/46
    The Revised Project Management Arrangements for Sizewell B.
    January 1984. 16pp; inc. appendix. (1 Addendum).

GEORGE, B. V.   CEGB/P/47
    The management of the Sizewell B project. April 1984. 95pp;
    appendices. (6 Addenda).

CENTRE FOR ENERGY STUDIES   CES 01
    Statement of Case. Polytechnic of the South Bank. September 1983. 6pp.

SWEET, C.   CES/P/1
    Some lessons from the French nuclear power experience that the UK
    might learn. October 1983. 34pp. (1 Addendum).

FINE, B.   CES/P/2
    The future of coal prices. October 1983. 22pp.

PAPADOPOULOS, R.   CES/P/3
    Electricity Industry in England and Wales: Policy decisions and
    future needs. October 1983. 6pp. (1 Addendum).

GILES, R.   CES/P/4
    Some Comments on Energy Demand Elasticities. October 1983. 9pp.

CHAPMAN, E. S.   ESC 01
    Statement by Mr and Mrs E S Chapman. September 1984. 1p.

COMMUNIST PARTY: EAST ANGLIAN DISTRICT COMMITTEE   CP:EADC 01
    Statement of Case. April 1983. 7pp. (1 Addendum).

COMMUNIST PARTY OF GREAT BRITIAN: LEISTON BRANCH   CP: LB 01
    Statement. October 1984. 4pp.

CONCERNS AGAINST NUCLEAR TECHNOLOGY ORGANISATION

HANSON, J.   CANTO/P/1
    Proof of evidence. September 1984. 2pp.

COUNCIL FOR THE PROTECTION OF RURAL ENGLAND   CPRE 01
    The Economic Case Against Sizewell B: Statement of Case to be advanced
    by CPRE against the CEGB's power station proposal, Sizewell B Public
    Inquiry. January 1983. 17pp.

KOMANOFF, C.   CPRE/P/1
    Capital costs, construction times and operating performance of
    Westinghouse PWR's. May 1983. 80pp; separate vol. of tables.
    (4 Addenda).

JOHNSON, R. H.   CPRE/P/2
    Fossil Fuel Prices. May 1983. 70pp; separate vol. of tables.

JOHNSON, R. H.   CPRE/P/2 (REV)
   Fossil Fuel Prices.   June 1983.   66pp, inc. appendices.
   (4 Addenda).

BARRETT, M.   CPRE/P/3
   Energy Conservation and Peak Electricity Demand. May 1983. 63pp;
   separate vol. of appendices. (6 Addenda).

CORY, B. J.   CPRE/P/4
   Load management and peak electricity demand. May 1983. 32pp;
   separate vol. of tables. (1 Addendum).

WILKINS, B.   CPRE/P/5
   Industrial Combined Heat and Power Generation. May 1983. 43pp;
   separate vol. of appendice. (2 Addenda).

NECTOUX, F.   CPRE/P/6
   Planning margin and generation supply security. May 1983. 30pp;
   separate vol. of tables. (2 Addenda).

CONROY, C.   CPRE/P/7
   The Economic Case For Not Ordering Sizewell B. May 1983. 47pp;
   separate vol. of appendices. (4 Addenda).

DEPARTMENT OF ENERGY

PRIDDLE, R. J.   DEN/P/1
   Concerning the Government's approach to energy supply and demand, and
   electricity. 1982. 5pp; Annex on Energy Projections. 46pp. (8 Addenda).

DEPARTMENT OF THE ENVIRONMENT

WEDD, G.   DOE/P/1
   Concerning radioactive waste management policy. 1982. 17pp. (5 Addenda).

HOOKWAY, B.   DOE/P/2
   Concerning radioactive waste managment - technical matters. 1982.
   16pp. (6 Addenda).

DEPARTMENT OF TRANSPORT

O'SULLIVAN, R. A.   DTp/P/1
   Safety arrangements for the transport of radioactive material. 1982.
   8pp; appendices. (2 Addenda).

DRYE, D. J.   DJD 01
   Statement of Case March 1983. 4pp. (2 Addenda).

ELECTRICITY CONSUMERS COUNCIL   ECC 01
   Statement of Case, February 1983. 40pp; appendix.

BARNES, M.   ECC/P/1
   Electricity Consumers' Council Policy. June 1983. 10pp.

- 7 -

MACKERRON, G.   ECC/P/2
    Construction Times and Costs. June 1983. 45pp. (2 Addenda).

THOMAS, S   ECC/P/3
    Plant Related Variables: Plant Operation. June 1983. 34pp. (3 Addenda).

JONES, I. S.   ECC/P/4
    Fossil Fuel Prices. June 1983. 52pp.

JONES, I. S.   ECC/P/4 (REV)
    Fossil Fuel Prices. September 1983. 83pp. (4 Addenda).

JONES, I. S.   ECC/P/5
    Deferment. June 1983. 25pp. (2 Addenda).

MACKERRON, G.   ECC/P/6
    Fuel Diversity and Security of Electricity Supply. June 1983. 29pp.

THOMAS, S.   ECC/P/7
    Technology Choice and Transfer. June 1983. 35pp. (1 Addendum).

JONES, I. MACKERRON, G. AND THOMAS, S.   ECC/P/8
    Overall Technical Assessment of the Economic Benefit Case. June 1983.
    14pp. (1 Addendum).

THE ERGONOMICS SOCIETY   ES 01
    Statement of Case. 1982. 12pp.

HALE, A. R.   ES/P/1
    Operating Goals, Allocation of Function, Task Definition, Job Design, and
    Operation Experience.

BAINBRIDGE, L.   ES/P/2
    Interface, Workplace Conditions, and Support Documentation.

DUNCAN, K. D.   ES/P/3
    Selection and Training.

EMBREY, D. E.   ES/P/4
    Human Reliability, and Quality Assurance.

    The Ergonomics Society's Proofs of Evidence, ES/P/1-4 are contained in
    1 volume. January 1983. 52pp. (5 Addenda).

FOSTER, J.   JF 01
    Statement. November 1984. 1p.

FRAME, A.   AGF/P/1
    Proof of evidence. September 1983. 27pp. (4 Addenda).

FRIENDS OF THE EARTH   FOE 01
    Statement of Case for Friends of the Earth. September 1983. 32pp.

KJELLSTROM, B.   FOE/P/1
    Safety criteria and uncertainties in reactor fault transient analysis.
    January 1984. 123pp, inc. appendices.

HAHN, L.   FOE/P/2
    Probabilistic safety analysis for Sizewell B.   January 1984.   191pp.
    (3 Addenda).

MINOR,   G. C.   FOE/P/3
    Generic safety issues, systems interaction, human error, sabotage and
    incredible events.   December 1983.   58pp.   (1 Addendum).

GREEN, C.   FOE/P/4
    The justification of the CEGB's fundamental reliability criteria.
    December 1983.   66pp.   (3 Addenda).

PATTERSON, W. C.   FOE/P/5
    Sizewell B and its implications for nuclear proliferation.
    January 1984.   18pp.   (1 Addendum).

GREATER LONDON COUNCIL   GLC 01
    Statement of Case.   February 1983.   20pp.

HUTCHINSON, D   GLC/P/1
    GLC interest in electricity supply.   October 1983.   29pp; figures.
    (6 Addenda).

MACADAM, J. A.   GLC/P/2
    The Development of Combined Heat and Power with District Heating in
    London.   GLC.   October 1983.   60pp; appendix.   (9 Addenda).

MOORCRAFT, C. AND HODGKINSON, S.   GLC/P/3
    Public Sector Investment in Domestic Energy Conservation Versus
    Investment in Sizewell B.   October 1983.   141pp; inc. tables.

MOORCRAFT, C. AND HODGKINSON, S.   GLC/P/3 (REV)
    Public Sector Investment in Domestic Energy Conservation Versus
    Investment in Sizewell B.   October 1983.   141pp; tables.   (4 Addenda).

NECTOUX, F.   GLC/P/4
    Electricity Use in London and Potential for Electricity Conservation.
    October 1983.   54pp.   (3 Addenda).

MASON, N. C.   GLC/P/5
    The Macroeconomic and Employment Effects of Different Energy Investment
    Options.   October 1983.   99pp.   (6 Addenda).

SLATER, D.   GLC/P/6A & B
    Assessment of the Impact on the Greater London Population of an
    Accidental Release of Radioactivity from the Sizewell B PWR.   GLC.
    March 1984.   2 Vols.   (6 Addenda).
    A.   Proof of evidence.   106pp; appendix 1 .
    B.   Appendices 2-10.   2 Vols.

SLATER, D.   GLC/P/7
    Assessment of the impact on the Greater London Population of a
    release of radioactivity during transportation of spent fuel.
    July 1984.   51pp; appendices.   (3 Addenda).

CROLL, J.   GLC/P/8
    Structural integrity of irradiated fuel transportation flasks.   July 1984.
    111pp; inc. figures.   (4 Addenda).

INNES, G.   GLC/P/9
   Emergency planning for major accidents at the proposed Sizewell B
   PWR nuclear power station and for trains carrying irradiated fuel from
   existing nuclear power stations through London. April 1984. 99pp;
   inc. appendices. (2 Addenda).

BUCHAN, K. A.   GLC/P/10
   Transport of irradiated fuel by rail - proposals for establishing
   alternative routes. July 1984. 22pp; maps. (1 Addendum).

PETERKEN, L. E.   GLC/P/11
   Greater London Council policy concerning the proposed Sizewell B
   PWR nuclear power station. October 1984. 36pp; appendix. (1 Addendum).

HARDMAN, A. E.   AEH/P/1
   Proof of evidence. May 1984.

HOLMES, W.   WH 01
   Statement. October 1984. 2pp.

   HOLMES, W   WH 01 (REV)
   Revised statement. November 1984. 3pp.

ION, D. C.   ION/P/1
   A review of the availability of world energy resources. 17 June 1984.
   36pp. (5 Addenda).

IPSWICH BOROUGH COUNCIL et al.

   CANN, J. C.   IBC/P/1 (REVISED)
   Statement on behalf of the Councils of the Borough of Ipswich and the
   Cities of Cambridge and Norwich. October 1984. 5pp.

IPSWICH FRIENDS OF THE EARTH   IDF 01
   The extent and nature of public opposition to more nuclear power
   stations, as shown by recent surveys of public attitudes. November 1984.
   2pp.

   SADLER, R. AND SPENCER, L.   IDF/P/1
   The extent and nature of public opposition to more nuclear power stations,
   as shown by recent surveys of public attitudes. November 1984. 14pp.

JENKINS, N.   NJ/P/1

   Proof of evidence. September 1984. 5pp. (2 Addenda).

JOINT ECOLOGY PARTIES   JEP 01
   Statement of Case. January 1984. 5pp.

   OUBRIDGE, G. E.   JEP/P/1
   Proof of evidence. May 1984. 39pp. (1 Addendum).

   GOLDSTICK, M.   JEP/P/2
   Proof of evidence. May 1984. 127pp.

GRAHAM, J.   JEP/P/3
    Proof of evidence. May 1984. 11pp.

ALDRIDGE, A.   JEP/P/4
    Proof of evidence. May 1984. 53pp.

HENDRY, L. M.   JEP/P/5
    Uranium supplies and related issues. April 1984. 23pp.

FLICK, B.   JEP/P/6
    Proof of evidence. May 1984. 5pp.

TREGANZA, J.   JEP/P/7
    Proof of evidence. May 1984. 4pp.

JOINT PARISH COUNCILS

THRING, M. W.   JPC/P/1
    The Case Against Building a PWR at Sizewell. January 1984. 33pp.
    (1 Addendum).

FLAVIN, C.   JPC/P/2
    Nuclear Power: The Market Test (Worldwatch Paper 57). January 1984.
    88pp. (2 Addenda).

ZEIGLER, D. J.   JPC/P/3
    The emergency planning for nuclear stations. November 1984. 4pp;
    appendices.

REED, S. R.   JPC/P/4
    Proof of evidence. November 1984. 2 Vols.
    A. Vol.1.   Proof of evidence and statement from Fire Chief
                 Donald H. Konkle. 29pp.
    B. Vol.2.   Appendices. 123pp.

SINGLETON, R. D.   JPC/P/5
    Sizewell B: Transportation Aspects. November 1984. 2 Vols. (2 Addenda).
    A. Vol.1.   Proof of evidence. 87pp.
    B. Vol.2.   Appendices.

KLETZ, T. A.   TAK/P/1
    The use of quantitative methods in risk assessment. May 1984. 41pp.
    (1 Addendum).

LANGLEY, E. H.   EHL/P/1
    Statement concerning the siting of Westinghouse type nuclear reactor at
    Sizewell, Suffolk. March 1983. 17pp; appendices.

LEISTON TOWN COUNCIL   LTC 01
    Statement by Robert L. Morris, Town Clerk, Leiston on behalf of Leiston
    Town Council. October 1984. 13pp. (2 Addenda).

MICHAELS, M. I.   MIM/P/1
    A discussion of the major topics relating to the construction of
    Sizewell B. February 1983. 40pp.

MINISTRY OF AGRICULTURE, FISHERIES AND FOOD

CHAMBERLAIN, P. D.   MAFF/P/1
    Implications for Government policy for the protection of agricultural
    land. 1982. 4pp; appendices. (1 Addendum).

NEILSON, H. R.   MAFF/P/2
    Radioactive waste disposal policy. 1982. 9pp; inc appendix. (3 Addenda).

MEEKINGS, G. F.   MAFF/P/3
    Agricultural implications of radioactive waste disposal. 1982. 16pp.
    (2 Addenda).

MITCHELL, N. T.   MAFF/P/4
    Technical aspects of the disposal of radioactive wastes to sea. 1982.
    23pp; tables, figure. (2 Addenda).

MURRELL, H.   HM 01
    An ordinary citizen's view of radioactive waste management. August
    1984. 14pp; appendix.

NATIONAL COAL BOARD

PARKER, M. J.   NCB/P/1
    Coal Price Prospects and Availability of Coal in the UK. Power
    Generation Market. February 1983. 19pp; inc appendix. (7 Addenda).

NATIONAL NUCLEAR CORPORATION LTD
                                                                          NNC 01
    Statement of Case. 1982. 28pp; two appendices.

FRANKLIN, N. L.   NNC/P/1
    Proof of evidence. 1983. 92pp; inc. appendices. (7 Addenda).

PUGH, C. D.   NNC/P/2
    Proof of evidence. March 1983. 76pp. (2 Addenda).

NATIONAL RADIOLOGICAL PROTECTION BOARD

CLARKE, R. H.   NRPB/P/1
    The status and functions of the NRPB. February 1983. 12pp.

POCHIN, SIR EDWARD   NRPB/P/2
    The Biological Bases of the Assumptions made by NRPB in the Calculations
    of Health Effects. June 1983. 34pp.

POCHIN, SIR EDWARD   NRPB/P/2 (REVISED)
    The Biological Bases of the Assumptions made by NRPB in the Calculation
    of Health Effects. November 1983. 70pp. (2 Addenda).

WEBB, G. A. M.   NRPB/P/3
    The requirement to keep radiation exposures As Low As Reasonably
    Achievable (ALARA). October 1984. 12pp. (1 Addendum).

NATIONAL UNION OF MINEWORKERS   NUM 01
     Statement of Case. October 1983. 16pp.

  FOTHERGILL, S., GUDGIN, G. AND MASON, N.   NUM/P/1
     The Sizewell B Nuclear Power Station and its consequences for the UK
     economy. October 1983. 55pp; appendix. (1 Addendum).

  BENN, T.   NUM/P/2
     Proof of evidence. November 1983. 16pp.

  MOURE, R.   NUM/P/3
     Health and safety issues on the front end of the nuclear fuel cycle.
     May 1984. 24pp.

  TAYLOR, P. AND KAYES, R.   NUM/P/4
     A comparison of the health and safety implications of the coal and
     nuclear fuel cycles. June 1984. 8pp.

NATURE CONSERVANCY COUNCIL

  SHACKLES, C. J. D.   NAT/P/1
     Proof of evidence. November 1984. 3pp. (2 Addenda).

NORFOLK COUNTY LABOUR PARTY   NCLP 01
     Submission to Inquiry into the CEGB proposal to build a PWR at Sizewell.
     1982. 8pp.

  ROUND, R. G.   NCLP/P/1
     Some Aspects of the Relative Costs of the Proposed PWR and AGR's.
     November 1983. 9pp. (1 Addendum).

  ROUND, R. G.   NCLP/P/2
     Safety comparisons between the proposed PWR and AGR's. March 1984.
     8pp; figures. (3 Addenda).

NORTHUMBERLAND COUNTY COUNCIL   NCC 01
     Statement of Case. March 1983. 12pp. (1 Addendum).

NORTHUMBERLAND AND NEWCASTLE SOCIETY   N & N SOC 01
     Statement of Case. June 1983. 11pp.

  NORTHUMBERLAND AND NEWCASTLE SOCIETY   N & N SOC/P/1
     Proof of evidence. July 1983. 31pp.

  NUCLEAR INSTALLATIONS INSPECTORATE   NII 01
     Sizewell B: A reivew by HM Nuclear Installations Inspectorate of the
     Pre-Construction Safety Report. London: HMSO, 1982. 88pp.
     Supplement 1 : Degraded core analysis.   NII 01 (Supp 1)
             London: HMSO, 1982. 17pp.
     Supplement 2 : Safety Analysis.   NII 01 (Supp 2)
             London: HMSO, 1982, 18pp.
     Supplement 3 : External Hazards - Aircraft Crash. 11pp. NII 01 (Supp 3)
     Supplement 4 : Steam Generator Tube Integrity. 8pp.   NII 01 (Supp 4)
     Supplement 5 : Fuel Clad Ballooning. 23pp; figures.   NII 01 (Supp 5)
     Supplement 6 : Reactor Protection System. 22pp.   NII 01 (Supp 6)

Supplement 7 : External Hazards - Earthquake. 11pp.   NII 01 (Supp 7)
Supplement 8 : External Hazards - Fire. 21pp; figures.   NII 01 (Supp 8)
Supplement 9 : Code Validation for LOCA. 19pp.   NII 01 (Supp 9)
Supplement 10: Reactor Pressure Vessel. 18pp.   NII 01 (Supp 10)
Supplement 11: Pressure Circuit Components. 14pp.   NII 01 (Supp 11)
Supplement 12: ALARP strategy for dose reduction. 41pp.   NII 01 (Supp 12)
Supplement 13: Human Factors. 10pp.   NII 01 (Supp 13)
Supplement 14: Quality Assurance. 8pp.   NII 01 (Supp 14)

(Supplements 3-14: published London: HMSO, 1983)

ANTHONY, R. D.   NII/P/1
    Work and responsibilities of HM Nuclear Installations Inspectorate.
    March 1983. 87pp; inc. appendices. (13 Addenda).

WOODS, P. B.   NII/P/2
    Nuclear Installations Inspectorate's View of the Central Electricity
    Generating Board's safety case. March 1983. 138pp. (20 Addenda).

OLIVER, D.   DO 01
    Statement. October 1984. 4pp.

PILKINGTON, N. M.   NMP/P/1
    Sizewell B and the proliferation of Nuclear Weapons. September 1983.
    28pp.

PORTSKEWETT ACTION GROUP   PAG 01
    Statement of Case. January 1983. 6pp.

    HANCOCK, G. H.   PAG/P/1
        Proof of evidence on safety issues. February 1984. 27pp; figures.

POWELL, M. B.   MBP/P/1
    Proof of evidence. November 1984. 19pp.

PRO NUCLEAR POWER PEOPLE   PNPP 01
    Statement of Case. 1983. 1p.

RIDGEWAY CONSULTANTS (DR K LITTLE)   KL 01
    Statement of Case. April 1983. 7pp.

    LITTLE, K.   KL/P/1
        The Nuclear Power Programme in Context. April 1983. 47pp.

    PLANE, A. S.   KL/P/2
        Problems posed by industrial monopoly formation. April 1983. 10pp.
        Not allocated   KL/P/3

    LITTLE, K.   KL/P/4
        The biological mechanisms of radiation injuries their significance for
        the safety case. April 1983. 97pp; figures.

    WARD, H. G.   KL/P/5
        Factors influencing public opinion. April 1983. 12pp.

ROPE, R. G. A.　　　　　　　　　　　　　　　　　　　　　　　　　　ROPE/P/1
　　　Proof of evidence on environmental matters affecting adjacent agri-
　　　cultural land.　September 1984.　10pp.

ROSENTHAL, R.　　　　　　　　　　　　　　　　　　　　　　　　　　RR 01
　　　Statement of Case.　October 1983.　2pp.

　ROSENTHAL, R.　　　　　　　　　　　　　　　　　　　　　　　　　　RR/P/1
　　　The Sizewell B PWR and Namibian Uranium.　May 1984.　23pp.

　PICKERING, A.　　　　　　　　　　　　　　　　　　　　　　　　　　RR/P/2
　　　Namibian Uranium.　May 1984.　3pp.

　PICCIOTTI, S.　　　　　　　　　　　　　　　　　　　　　　　　　　RR/P/3
　　　The Sizewell B PWR and Namibian Uranium International Legal Aspects.
　　　May 1984.　31pp; inc appendices.

ROSS, D.　　　　　　　　　　　　　　　　　　　　　　　　　　　　DR/P/1
　　　Proof of evidence.　July 1983.　43pp.　(1 Addendum).

ROYAL INSTITUTE OF BRITISH ARCHITECTS: EASTERN REGION BRANCH　　RIBA:ER 01
　　　Statement of Case.　March 1983.　6pp.

　CARTER, J.　　　　　　　　　　　　　　　　　　　　　　　　　RIBA:ER/P/1
　　　Submission to Sizewell B Power Station Public Inquiry by the Royal
　　　Institute of British Architects Eastern Region.　March 1984.　28pp.
　　　(2 Addenda).

SOUTH OF SCOTLAND ELECTRICITY BOARD

　MILLER, D. J.　　　　　　　　　　　　　　　　　　　　　　　　　　SSEB/P/1
　　　The economic merits of the AGR.　May 1984.　33pp; figures and tables.
　　　(1 Addendum).

　MILLER, D. J.　　　　　　　　　　　　　　　　　　　　　　　　　　SSEB/P/2
　　　The licensing of future AGR's.　May 1984.　7pp.

　MILLER, D. J.　　　　　　　　　　　　　　　　　　　　　　　　　　SSEB/P/3
　　　The supply of heat to large district heating schemes from AGR's.
　　　May 1984.　32pp; inc figures and diagrams.

**SOUTH YORKSHIRE, WEST YORKSHIRE, NOTTINGHAMSHIRE AND
DERBYSHIRE COUNTY COUNCILS**　　　　　　　　　　　　　　　　　　　YND 01
　　　Statement of Case.　July 1983.　10pp.

　PATTERSON, K.　　　　　　　　　　　　　　　　　　　　　　　　　　YND/P/1
　　　Nuclear Power and the Economies and Communities of the Four Counties.
　　　South Yorkshire, West Yorkshire, Nottinghamshire and Derbyshire County
　　　Councils.　October 1983.　24pp; tables.　(2 Addenda).

STEARN, R. F.　　　　　　　　　　　　　　　　　　　　　　　　　STN 01
　　　Submission to the Sizewell B Inquiry.　December 1984.　2pp.

STERNE, R.   RFS 01
     Statement of Case. October 1983. 3pp. (2 Addenda).

STONER, G. B.   GS/P/1
     Advantages of an appropriate and non-proliferating energy strategy.
     May 1983. 54pp; inc appendices. (2 Addenda).

STOP SIZEWELL B ASSOCIATION AND ECOROPA   SSBA 01
     Statement of Case.
     Part One : Need and Economics. July 1983. 18pp.   SSBA 01A
     Part Two : Safety. January 1985. 7pp.   SSBA 01B
     Part Three: Local Implications. January 1985. 4pp.   SSBA 01C

   JEFFERY, J. W.   SSBA/P/1
     An Economic Critique of the CEGB's Case for a PWR at Sizewell. November
     1983. 77pp. (7 Addenda).

   BUNYARD, P. P.   SSBA/P/2
     The Need for Sizewell B and the Economics of the Fuel Cycle. February
     1984. 46pp. (1 Addendum).

   MARSHALL, R.   SSBA/P/3
     The Optimal Performance of Energy Tasks: Matching the Quality of Energy
     Supply to Energy Demand, with particular reference to Space Heating.
     November 1983. 20pp.

   JEFFERY, J. W.   SSBA/P/4
     The unique dangers of nuclear power. June 1984. 44pp.

   BLACKITH, R. E.   SSBA/P/5
     Leukaemia incidences. July 1984. 29pp; appendices. (4 Addenda).

   STUART, M.   SSBA/P/6
     The statistical significance of leukaemia incidence at Sizewell A.
     July 1984. 6pp.

   STEWART, A.   SSBA/P/7
     Uncertainties of the effects of low-dose radiation. October 1984. 4pp.

   BERTELL, R.   SSBA/P/8
     The human health consequences of exposure to ionising radiation.
     August 1984. 66pp. (1 Addendum).

   PICKETT, J.   SSBA/P/9
     The local implications of Sizewell B. November 1984. 26pp.

   CHADWICK, L.   SSBA/P/10
     The ecological case against Sizewell B. June 1984. 28pp; inc appendix.
     (1 Addendum).

   BUNYARD, P. P.   SSBA/P/11
     A comparison between Sellafield and La Hague. September 1984. 20pp

   BARNABY, F.   SSBA/P/12
     Consequences of the plutonium economy. November 1984. 40pp.

SUFFOLK COMMITTEE OF TWO FOR FAIR PLAY   SCTFP 01
        Statement of Case. May 1984. 2pp.

SUFFOLK COUNTY AND COASTAL DISTRICT COUNCILS   LPA 01 (REVISED)
        Statement of Case for Sizewell B. 1983. 9pp.

BARRITT, E. E.   LPA/P/1
        Concerning local environmental issues. 1982. 37pp; appendices.
        (5 Addenda).

RATCLIFFE, K.   LPA/P/2 (REVISED)
        Noise implications of construction and operation. March 1983. 32pp;
        maps. (2 Addenda).

LESLIE, D. C.   LPA/P/3
        Concerning safety issues. March 1983. 184pp. (7 Addenda).

KUSSMAUL, K. F.   LPA/P/4
        Concerning the structural integrity of the primary circuit. April 1983.
        3 Vols. (2 Addenda).
        Vol 1: Proof of evidence. 54pp.   LPA/P/4A
        Vol 2: Appendices.   LPA/P/4B
        Vol 3: Figures and tables.   LPA/P/4C

SAYLES, R. S.   LPA/P/5
        Concerning the assessment of the Probabilistic Safety Analysis made for
        Sizewell B. April 1983. 55pp; inc. appendices. (3 Addenda).

SUFFOLK PRESERVATION SOCIETY   SPS 01
        Statement of Case, Part One.   June 1984. 5pp.   SPS 01 A
                            Part Two.   October 1984. 3pp.   SPS 01B
                                                                                      SPS/P/1
BLYTHE, R.
        The unique quality and feature of the Suffolk coast. October 1984.
        7pp; appendices.

MOGGRIDGE, H.   SPS/P/2
        Landscape matters. October 1984. 10pp; appendices. (2 Addenda).

RANDALL, R.   SPS/P/3
        Ecology and the alternative road routes to the Sizewell B site. October
        1984. 18pp; inc. appendices. (1 Addendum).

RANSON, C.   SPS/P/4
        Ecology - the importance of the Sizewell Belts area. October 1984. 6pp.

ROUND, R. G.   SPS/P/5
        An assessment of the benefit to electricity users in the south of
        England and Wales in terms of improved security and quality of supply by
        siting the proposed generating station in the South West. June 1984.
        11pp; inc. figures. (3 Addenda).

PARKER, G. B.   SPS/P/6
        Proof of evidence. October 1984. 2pp. (1 Addendum).

WOODHAMS, P.   SPS/P/7
        Local environmental issues - commentary on the planning perspective.
        November 1984. 52pp; inc. appendices.

THRING, J. B.   JBT/P/1 (REVISED)
    Proof of evidence. July 1983. 4pp. (2 Addenda).

TOWN AND COUNTRY PLANNING ASSOCIATION   TCPA 01
    Statement of Case. April 1983. 35pp.

    ODELL, P.   TCPA/P/1
        The future supply and price of oil. September 1983. 40pp. (4 Addenda).

    STEENBLIK, R.   TCPA/P/2
        The Price of Coal. September 1983. 33pp. (4 Addenda).

    PRIOR, M.   TCPA/P/3
        Aspects concerning Fossil Fuels. September 1983. 48pp. (1 Addendum).

    CROWTHER, S.   TCPA/P/4
        Social Costs of a Nuclear Power Programme. September 1983. 46pp; figures.

    INCE, M.   TCPA/P/5
        Implications for the British Power Plant Manufacturing Industry.
        September 1983. 30pp. (3 Addenda).

    SWEET, C.   TCPA/P/6
        Some Policy Implications of the Proposal to Build Sizewell B.
        September 1983. 64pp. (4 Addenda).

    THOMPSON, G.   TCPA/P/7
        Safety and Waste Management Implications of the Sizewell PWR.
        February 1984. 49pp.

    RESNIKOFF, M.   TCPA/P/8
        Transportation of Irradiated Fuel. January 1984. 31pp. (1 Addendum).

    FORDHAM, R. F.   TCPA/P/9
        The Risk of Explosion of the Sizewell B Reactor Pressure Vessel.
        February 1984. 80pp; inc appendices. (2 Addenda).

WANSBECK DISTRICT COUNCIL   WDC 01
    Statement of Case. 1982. 5pp.

WEIR, LORD   WG/P/1
    The Weir Group's experience in exporting components for PWR's. January
    1984. 4pp.

WELSH ANTI NUCLEAR ALLIANCE
    ROWNTREE, P. M.   WANA/P/1
        The Case Against Sizewell B. The Credibility of the CEGB. November 1983.
        10pp.

    RICHARDS, H. W.   WANA/P/2
        The Case Against Sizewell B. November 1983. 34pp; appendices.

WILKS, A.   AW/P/1
    Proof of evidence. July 1983. 10pp.

WILLIAMSON, J.   JW/P/1
    The outlook for the future sterling real exchange rate. May 1984. 29pp.
    (3 Addenda).

WILSON, E. M.   EMW/P/1
    The Case for the Severn Barrage. June 1983. 11pp; inc tables.

WILSON, H.   HW 01
    Statement to the Sizewell B Inquiry. December 1984. 3pp.

LIST OF DOCUMENTS INTRODUCED BY COUNSEL TO THE INQUIRY

DURING HIS CROSS-EXAMINATION OF WITNESSES

COUNSEL TO THE INQUIRY DOCUMENTS

COUNSEL TO THE INQUIRY   CI/1(NE)
Tables for the cross-examination of the Department of Energy.
16 March 1983. 23p.

Section 1: Pages 1-16 : Collation
Section 2: Pages 17-23: Other Forecasts.

COUNSEL TO THE INQUIRY   CI/1(NE)(REV)
Tables for the cross-examination of the Department of Energy.
27 May 1983. 23pp.

    Section 1: Pages 1-16 : Collation
    Section 2: Pages 17-23: Other Forecasts.

NUCLEAR POWER PROGRAMME   CI/2(GEN)
Debate on the Nuclear Power Programme.
(IN House of Commons, Official Report, 1 February 1982.
Cols 41-44.)

ENERGY POLICY   CI/3(GEN)
Energy Policy: A Consultative Document.
Presented by the Secretary of State for Energy to parliament.
London: HMSO, February 1978. 127, inc annex.

TOKYO SUMMIT CONFERENCE   CI/4(NE)
Declaration: Tokyo Summit conference.
Tokyo, 28/29 June 1979. 6p.

DEPARTMENT OF ENERGY   CI/5(NE)
Energy Protections 1979. A paper by the Department of Energy.
Extract: Summary + p1-11.

BELVOIR INQUIRY   CI/6(NE)
Vale of Belvoir Coalfield Inquiry Report.
Presented to the Secretary of State for the Environment by
Mr Michael Mann QC.
London: HMSO, 26 November 1980. Extract: p13-23.
(ISBN 0 11 751502 7).

VALE OF BELVOIR   CI/7(NE)
Statement by Mr Heseltine, Secretary of State for the Environment,
on the Vale of Belvoir.
(IN House of Commons, Official Report, 25 March 1982.
Cols 1096-1105.)

WILSON, E M   CI/8(NE)
Letter from Prof E M Wilson to Sir Frank Layfield of 9 March 1983.
2p.

CHARLISH, G and BARLING, L   CI/9(NE)
'Light programme' takes a new meaning.
Plan to use Radio Four to control domestic electricity use.
Article by G Charlish and L Barling. 25 February 1983.
Source unknown. 1p.

COMMITTEE ON THE BIOLOGICAL EFFECTS OF IONISING
RADIATIONS   CI/10(SAF)
The effect on populations of exposure to low levels of ionizing
radiations.
1980. p135-150, 177-195, 211-213, 227-230, 249-251.

CEGB   CI/11(ENV)
Submission to the Commission on Energy and the Environment.
Topic 4: Combustion Residues.

CEGB, March 1980. p2-12, 20-24, Table 1 and Figure 2.

JUNGK, R   CI/12(GEN)
Nuclear State. 1970. p61.

PEARCE, D et al   CI/13(NE)
Decision making for energy futures.
Macmillan Press Ltd. 1979. p148-149.

DALYELL, T   CI/14(GEN)
Acid rain erodes our credibility.
(IN New Scientist, 24 February 1983. p535.)

WRIGHT, P   CI/15(GEN)
Article by P Wright on mysterious return of prehistoric marsh gas.
(IN The Times, 13 April 1983. 1p.)

THE ROYAL SOCIETY   CI/16(SAF)
Risk Assessment. Report of a Royal Society Study Group.
London, January 1983.
(ISBN 0 85403 208 8).

POWER PLANT INDUSTRY   CI/17(GEN)
Reply by Mr Norman Lamont, Under-Secretary of State for Energy to a
question by Mr Mike Thomas.
(IN House of Commons, Official Report, 30 April 1981.
Cols 1007-1010.)

SOUTH OF SCOTLAND ELECTRICITY BOARD   CI/18(GEN)
Report and Accounts 1981/82. (Extract).

COUNSEL TO THE INQUIRY   CI/19(GEN)
Schedule of CEGB Stations by Region in 1981-1982.
(Source: CEGB Statistical Year Book. pp6-8, 14.)
May 1983. 14pp.

CEGB   CI/20(GEN)
Location of power stations and supergrid development as at
March 1982.
CEGB, May 1983. 1 map.

HOUSE OF COMMONS: SELECT COMMITTEE ON ENERGY   CI/21(GEN)
Minutes of Evidence to the Select Committee on Energy. Evidence
from the CEGB and Northern Engineering Ltd. (Concerning CHP).
London: HMSO, 8 March 1982. (HC 60-vii). Extract: pp309-320.

HOUSE OF COMMONS: SELECT COMMITTEE ON ENERGY   CI/22(GEN)
Minutes of Evidence to the Select Committee on Energy. Evidence
from W S Atkins and Partners. (Concerning CHP).
London: HMSO, 6 December 1982. (HC 107). Extract: pp479-483.

DETTMER, R   CI/23(NE)
Embarras de richesses from French nuclear programme.
(IN IEE News, May 1983. 1p.)

MILITANT   CI/24(NE)
Engineering construction - What the agreement means.
(IN Militant, 6 May 1983. 1p.)

NATIONALISED INDUSTRIES   CI/25(NE)
Reply by Mr Lawson, Secretary of State for Energy, to a question
by Sir William Van Straubenzee about objectives of nationalised
industries.
(IN House of Commons, Official Report, 18 March 1983.
Cols 296-8.)

KECK, O   CI/26(GEN)
Industrial Policy for Nuclear Power: A comparison of West German
and British Experience.
(IN Issues in the Sizewell 'B' Inquiry. Vol 6.
Centre for Energy Studies. pp28-42.)

HOUSE OF COMMONS: SELECT COMMITTEE ON ENERGY   CI/27(NE)
Minutes of Evidence to the Select Committee on Energy: Combined
Heat and Power. Evidence from Sir Walter Marshall.
London: HMSO, 2 December 1982. (HC 91). Extract: pp36-37.

WEBB, J E   CI/28(GEN)
Space Age Management - The Large Scale Approach.
McGraw-Hill, 1969. (Extract).

DARNELL, H and DALE, M W   CI/29(NE)
Total Project Management: An integrated approach to the management
of capital investment projects. Institution of Mechnical Engineers.
Vol 196, No 36, 1982. pp337-346. (ISSN 0020 - 3483).

MOOLIN, F E Jur   CI/30(GEN)
The Effective Project Management Organisation for Giant Projects.
(IN The Successful Accomplishment of Giant Projects.
OYEZ-IBC Conference, London, 17-18 May 1978.) (Extract).

NUCLEAR INSTALLATIONS ACT 1965   CI/31(GEN)
Nuclear Installations Act 1965 etc (Repeals and Modifications)
Regulations 1974.
SI 1974, No 2056. pp8005-8010.

COUNSEL TO THE INQUIRY   CI/32(GEN)
Collection of extracts from legal cases, dictionaries and
text-books relating to the meaning of the words "Practicable"
and "Reasonably Practicable" in a safety context.
May 1983. 42pp.

ENGINEERING CONSTRUCTION EDC   CI/33(GEN)
Guidelines for the Mangement of Major Projects in the Process
Industries.
National Economic Development Office.
London: HMSO, 1982. 41pp, inc appendices.
(ISBN 0 7292 0524 X).

ENERGY ACT, 1983   CI/34(GEN)
London: HSMO, 1983. 34pp. (ISBN 0 10 542583 4).

GAMMON, M   CI/35(ENV)
UK experience in selecting and developing nuclear power station
sites.
(IN Nuclear Engineering International, September 1979.)

COUNSEL TO THE INQUIRY   CI/36(GEN)
Selection of letters and written representations submitted to the
Inquiry. June 1983. 352pp.

CARR, P J and WILLIAMSON, J L   CI/37(NE)
The Sullom Voe Success Story.
(IN Proc Instn Mech Engrs, Vol 196, 1982. pp239-258.)

COUNSEL TO THE INQUIRY   CI/38(NE)
US Capital Costs Calculated Using C Komanoff Formulae.
(Source: CPRE/P/1B, Table C.) June 1983. 1pp.

COUNSEL TO THE INQUIRY   CI/39(NE)
Selection of distribution curves. CI, July 1983. 2pp.

HOUSE OF COMMONS: SELECT COMMITTEE ON ENERGY   CI/40(NE)
Minutes of Evidence to the Select Committee on Energy: Combined
Heat and Power. Evidence from Midlands Electricity Board.
London: HMSO, 24 November 1981. (HC 60-i). (Extract).

HOUSE OF COMMONS: SELECT COMMITTEE ON ENERGY   CI/41(NE)
Minutes of Evidence to the Select Committee on Energy: Combined
Heat and Power. Evidence from Midlands Electricity Board.
London: HMSO, 11 May 1982. (HC 60-ix). (Extract).

HOUSE OF COMMONS: SELECT COMMITTEE ON ENERGY   CI/42(NE)
Minutes of Evidence to the Select Committee on Energy: Combined
Heat and Power. Evidence from The Marshall Committee.
London: HMSO, 3 February 1982. (HC 60-ii). (Extract).

PRINGLE, P and SPIGELMAN, J   CI/43(GEN)
The Nuclear Barons. The inside story of how they created our
nuclear nightmare.
London, 1982. (Extract). (ISBN 07181 20612).

COUNSEL TO THE INQUIRY   CI/44(SAF)
Tables of Solid/Vitrified Wastes Arising from Sizewell 'B'.
Prepared from CEGB and BNFL proofs for purposes of
cross-examination.
CI, July 1983. 3pp.

COUNSEL TO THE INQUIRY   CI/44(REV)
Tables of Solid/Vitrified Wastes Arising from Sizewell B. Prepared
from CEGB and BNFL proofs for purposes of cross-examination.
CI, 15 July 1983. 3pp.

WATERS, W G II   CI/45(NE)
Transportation and Market Prospects in the World Coal Trade.
(IN The Logistics and Transportation Review, Volume 18, No2,
1983. pp139-167.)

COUNSEL TO THE INQUIRY   CI/46(NE)
Comparison of Oil Price Projections. September 1983. 13pp.

COUNSEL TO THE INQUIRY   CI/46(ADD1)
Comparison of HFO Prices (in $/te) in CEGB/S/345 and CEGB/P/6(ADD8)
- page 16.
CI, October 1983. 1p.

COUNSEL TO THE INQUIRY   CI/46(ADD2)
Comments on "Comparison of Oil Price Projections" (CI/46(NE)) by
the Department of Energy.
CI, October 1983. 2pp.

COUNSEL TO THE INQUIRY   CI/46(REV)
Comparison of Oil Price Projections. February 1984. 13pp.

COUNSEL TO THE INQUIRY   CI/46(REV)(ADD1)
Comments on "Comparison of Oil Price Projections" (CI/46(REV)) by
the Department of Energy and CEGB. April 1984. 2pp.

COUNSEL TO THE INQUIRY   CI/47(NE)
Comparisons of Coal Price Projections. October 1983. 23pp.

COUNSEL TO THE INQUIRY   CI/47(ADD1)
Comments on "Comparison of Coal Price Projections" (CI/47) by
CEGB and Department of Energy, and economic parameters submitted
by Department of Energy in context of the ERG exercise.
CI, October 1983. 13pp.

COUNSEL TO THE INQUIRY   CI/47(ADD2)
Revision of table 6 - Cost Components of Coal Delivered to Europe
(ARA) in the year 2000 - in "Comparison of Coal Price Projections"
(CI/47).
CI, October 1983. 1p.

COUNSEL TO THE INQUIRY   CI/47(ADD3)
Comparison of Direct, and Trans-shipment Costs. (All prices in
p/GJ, March 1982 prices.)
CI, October 1983. 1p.

COUNSEL TO THE INQUIRY   CI/47(ADD4)
Comparison of CEGB, CPRE and Chase Econometrics Projections of
Minemouth Costs.
CI, October 1983. 3pp.

COUNSEL TO THE INQUIRY   CI/47(ADD5)
Comments on "Comparison of Coal Price Projections" (CI/47) by
the NCB.
CI, November 1983. 9pp.

COUNSEL TO THE INQUIRY   CI/47(REV)
Comparison of Coal Price Projections. February 1984. 30pp.

COUNSEL TO THE INQUIRY   CI/47(REV)(ADD1)
Comments on "Comparison of Coal Price Projections" (CI/47(REV)) by
M Prior (TCPA). February 1984. 2pp.

COUNSEL TO THE INQUIRY   CI/47(REV)(ADD2)
Comments on "Comparison of Coal Price Projections" (CI/47(REV)) by
NCB and CEGB. April 1984. 4pp.

COUNSEL TO THE INQUIRY   CI/48(NE)
OPEC Oil Reserves as Percentage of WOCA Oil Reserves.
CI, November 1983. 3pp.

FISHLOCK, D   CI/49(NE)
Nuclear Power: a race against time in Scotland.
(IN Financial Times, 25 May 1983. 2pp.)

COUNSEL TO THE INQUIRY   CI/50(SAF)
An Outline of the Scope of the Counsel to the Inquiry's
cross-examination of Sir Edward Pochin (NRPB/P/2 Revised).
CI, December 1983. 4pp.

BAVERSTOCK, K F and VENNART, J   CI/51(SAF)
Emergency Reference Levels for Reactor Accidents: A re-examination
of the Windscale Reactor Accident.
(IN Health Physics, Vol 30. Pergamon Press, April 1976.
pp339-344.)

EUROPEAN COMMUNITIES   CI/52(GEN)
Treaty establishing The European Atomic Energy Community:
As Amended by Subsequent Treaties.
Rome. 25 March 1957. (Cmnd 7462). Treaty Series No 17 (1979).
London: HMSO, 1979. (Extract). (SBN 010 174620 2).

ARDLEY, N   CI/53(SAF)
Atoms and Energy.
New Horizon Library, 1975. (Extract). (SBN 562 000143).

RYLE, C et al   CI/54(SAF)
Radiation.
Radiation and Health Information Service, March 1980. (Extract).

O'RIORDON, M C et al   CI/55(SAF)
Human Exposure to Radon Decay Products Inside Dwellings in the
United Kingdom.
NRPB-R152. February 1983. (Extract).

NEW SCIENTIST   CI/56(SAF)
Why the public ignores risk analysis.
(IN New Scientist, 1 September 1983. 1p.)

HARRISON, J D   CI/57(SAF)
Gut Uptake Factors for Plutonium, Americium and Curium.
NRPB-R129. January 1982. (Extract).

CONNOR, S   CI/58(SAF)
Science behind civil defence planning is condemned.
(IN New Scientist, 24 November 1983. p559.)

UNSCEAR   CI/59(SAF)
Ionizing Radiation: Sources and Biological Effects.
United Nations Scientific Committee on the Effects of
Atomic Radiation.
Report to the General Assembly. 1982. (Extract).

REISSLAND, J A   CI/60(SAF)
Epidemiological Methods of Assessing Risks from Low Level
Occupational Exposure to Ionizing Radiation.
(IN Radiation Protection Dosimetry, Vol 2, No 4, 1982.
pp199-207.)

TAYLOR, P J   CI/61(SAF)
The Windscale Fire, October 1957.
Political Ecology Research Group. Research Report RR-7.
July 1981. (Extract). (ISBN 0142 7199).

DUNSTER, J   CI/62(SAF)
Are we too frightened of radiation?
(IN New Scientist, 13 October 1983. 1p.)

DUNSTER, J   CI/63(SAF)
Some Reactions to the Accident at Three Mile Island.
(IN Nuclear Energy, Vol 19, No 3, June 1980. pp139-146.)

COUNSEL TO THE INQUIRY   CI/64(SAF)
Counsel to the Inquiry: Questions on Safety Matters; outline of
the scope of Mr Brooke's cross-examination of Mr Anthony on NII/P/1.
CI, December 1983. 15pp.

COUNSEL TO THE INQUIRY   CI/65(NE)
Articles and letters on economics and the value of human life:
Your money or your life?
Marin, A. The Three Banks Review. June 1983. 18pp.
The price of life: where economics is out of its depth.
Broome, J. `Financial Times, 17 August 1983. 1p and 5 letters
arising from this article in the Financial Times dated 22 and
23 August and 2 and 6 September 1983.
CI, December 1983. 21pp.

US NUCLEAR REGULATORY COMMISSION   CI/66(SAF)
Safety Goals for Nuclear Power Plants: A Discussion Paper.
USNRC, NUREG-0880: For comment. February 1982. (Various pagings).

US NUCLEAR REGULATORY COMMISSION   CI/67(SAF)
Safety Goals for Nuclear Power Plants.
USNRC, NUREG-0880-REV 1. May 1983. 108pp.

DEPARTMENT OF TRANSPORT   CI/68(NE)
Road Accident Costs 1981.
Highways Economics Note No 1. July 1982. 3pp, appendix.

HOUSE OF COMMONS: EMPLOYMENT COMMITTEE   CI/69(SAF)
Sixth Report from the Employment Committee: The Working of the
Health and Safety Commission and Executive: Achievements since the
Roben's Report. Together with the Proceedings of the Committee and
Minutes of Evidence taken before the Committee on 9, 16 and 23 June
and 6 July 1982 and appendices. 1981-82 Session. (HC-400).`
London: HMSO, 1982. (Extract).

ADVISORY COMMITTEE ON TRUNK ROAD ASSESSMENT   CI/70(SAF)
Report of the Advisory Committee on Trunk Road Assessment.
Chairman: Sir George Leitch. 1978. (Extract).

ANTHONY, R D   CI/71(SAF)
Safety goals for nuclear power plants: Ths position in the United
Kingdom. 1982. 10pp.

INTERNATIONAL COMMISSION ON RADIOLOGICAL PROTECTION   CI/72(SAF)
Cost-Benefit Analysis in the Optimization of Radiation Protection.
ICRP 37, Vol 10, No 2/3. 1983. (Extract). (ISBN 008 029817 6).

COUNSEL TO THE INQUIRY   CI/73(SAF)
Extract from Secretariat Key Events Table.
CI, January 1984. 4pp.

HEALTH AND SAFETY EXECUTIVE   CI/74(SAF)
Press Release. PWR Public Inquiry: Statement by the Health and
Safety Executive.
HSE, 20 January 1982. 2pp.

COUNSEL TO THE INQUIRY   CI/75(SAF)
Notes for cross-examination Computer Codes/LOCA to take place on
17 January 1984.
CI, 10 January 1984. 10pp.

HEALTH AND SAFETY COMMISSION   CI/76(SAF)
Report 1981/1982.
London: HMSO, 1982. (Extract). (ISBN 011883671 4).

COUNSEL TO THE INQUIRY   CI/77(SAF)
Incidents involving contamination of radioactive waste flasks.
February 1984. 23pp.

COUNSEL TO THE INQUIRY   CI/77(ADD1)
Addendum to "Incidents involving contamination of flasks used
to transport irradiated nuclear fuel."
July 1984. 24pp.

COUNSEL TO THE INQUIRY   CI/77(ADD2)
Incidents at nuclear installations in Britain.   September, 1984.
12 pp.

COUNSEL TO THE INQUIRY   CI/78(NE)
Comparison of Exchange Rate Projections. February 1984. 9pp.

COUNSEL TO THE INQUIRY   CI/78(ADD1)
Comments on "Comparison of Exchange Rate Projections" (CI/78) by
CEGB, Department of Energy and ECC. April 1984. 11pp.

COLLIER, J G et al   CI/79(SAF)
PWR pressure vessel integrity-design for safety.
(IN Nuclear Energy, Vol 21, No 6, December 1982. pp377-383.)

NICHOLS, R W   CI/80(SAF)
The role of non-destructive testing in relation to PWR vessel
integrity.
(IN Nuclear Energy, Vol 22, No 4, August 1983. pp231-238.)

IAEA/OECD   CI/81(SAF)
Defect, Detection and Sizing. Article on an IAEA/OECD Specialist
Meeting held at Ispra. 3-6 May 1983.
(IN Nuclear Energy, Vol 22, No 5, October 1983. pp295-299.)

COUNSEL TO THE INQUIRY   CI/82(SAF)
Evidence of Dr Bush - MFB/P/1(ADD1): Leukaemia in East Suffolk.
Note by Mr H Brooke QC. March 1984. 7pp.

IEEE SPECTRUM   CI/83(SAF)
Three Mile Island and the future of nuclear power.
(IN IEEE Spectrum, November 1979. pp30-42.)

COUNSEL TO THE INQUIRY   CI/84(SAF)
Schedule of CEGB submissions and NII responses.
March 1984. 14pp.

COUNSEL TO THE INQUIRY   CI/84(REV)
Schedule of CEGB submissions and NII responses.
March 1984. 21pp.

COUNSEL TO THE INQUIRY   CI/84(REV)(ADD1)
Schedule of CEGB submissions and NII responses on A and B issues.
Comments by NII. May 1984. 4pp.

COUNSEL TO THE INQUIRY   CI/84(REV)(ADD2)
Schedule of CEGB submissions and NII responses on A and B issues.
Comments by CEGB and further comments by NII. May 1984. 15pp.

COUNSEL TO THE INQUIRY   CI/84(REV2)
Schedule of CEGB submissions and NII responses: A and B issues.
May 1984. 25pp.

COUNSEL TO THE INQUIRY   CI/84(REV3)
Schedule of CEGB submissions and NII responses: A and B issues.
June 1984. 25pp.

COUNSEL TO THE INQUIRY   CI/84(REV4)
Schedule of CEGB submissions and NII responses: A and B issues.
18 July 1984. 25pp.

COUNSEL TO THE INQUIRY   CI/84(REV5)
Schedule of CEGB submissions and NII responses: A and B issues.
17 September, 1984.   25 pp.

COUNSEL TO THE INQUIRY   CI/84(REV6)
Schedule of CEGB submissions and NII responses: A and B issues.
23 October 1984.   25 pp.

COUNSEL TO THE INQUIRY   CI/84(REV7)
Schedule of CEGB submissions and NII responses: A and B issues.
8 November 1984.   25 pp.

COUNSEL TO THE INQUIRY   CI/84(REV8)
Schedule of CEGB submissions and NII responses: A and B issues.
28 November, 1984.   25 pp.

COUNSEL TO THE INQUIRY   CI/84(REV9)
Schedule of CEGB submissions and NII responses : A and B issues.
12 December 1984.   24 pp.

COUNSEL TO THE INQUIRY   CI/85(SAF)
Extract from WCAP-9991 (CEGB/S/123) for use by Counsel to the
Inquiry in cross-examination.
March 1984. 15pp.

COUNSEL TO THE INQUIRY   CI/86(GEN)
Schedule of some significant dates. March 1984. 14pp.

DAVIES, L M   CI/87(SAF)
The Three Mile Island Incident.
Atomic Energy Technical Unit, Harwell, October 1979. 8pp.

WHITFIELD, D J C   CI/88(SAF)
Letter of 6 March 1974 to M Herbert, CEGB, from D J C Whitfield,
Ergonomics Society, about cross-examination of B V George on
CEGB/P/10. 21pp.

POPHAM, J   CI/89(ENV)
Letter of 16 December 1983 from J Popham, Suffolk Preservation
Society, to R K Drew, CEGB, about a proposed new access road to
Sizewell site. 3pp.

BURCHELL, M D   CI/90(ENV)
Letter of 6 January 1984 from M D Burchell, Countryside Commission,
to Inquiry Secretariat, about local environmental issues. 8pp.

DREW, R K   CI/91(ENV)
Letter of 5 April 1984 from R K Drew, CEGB, to J Popham, Suffolk
Preservation Society, about Sizewell 'B' - access road. 4pp.

DREW, R K   CI/92(ENV)
Letter of 5 April 1984 from R K Drew, CEGB, to M D Burchell,
Countryside Commission, about local environmental issues. 2pp.

COUNSEL TO THE INQUIRY   CI/93(SAF)
Notes for cross-examination of J Gittus (CEGB/P/16), P T McInerney
(CEGB/P/19), T Healey and S Board (CEGB/P/37), J R Harrison
(CEGB/P/11 and 45) and P B Woods (NII/P/2).
April 1984. 10pp.

COUNSEL TO THE INQUIRY   CI/93(ADD1)
Further notice of Mr Brooke's cross-examination of Mr McInerney
(CEGB/P/19).
May 1984. 2pp.

COUNSEL TO THE INQUIRY   CI/93(ADD2)
Advance notice to cross-examine Mr Woods (NII/P/2) and Mr Harrison
(CEGB/P/11 and P/45).
August 1984. 1p.

COUNSEL TO THE INQUIRY   CI/93(ADD3)
Third advance notice to cross-examine Mr. Woods (NII/P/2), and
Mr. Harrison (CEGB/P/11 and P/45) (see CI/93 and (ADD 2)).
September, 1984.   2 pp.

COUNSEL TO THE INQUIRY   CI/93(ADD3) (REV)
Third advance notice to cross-examine Mr. Woods (NII/P/2), and
Mr. Harrison (CEGB/P/11 and P/45) (see CI/93 and (ADD 2)).
September, 1984.   2 pp.

COUNSEL TO THE INQUIRY   CI/94(SAF)
Design definition and safety clearance. A paper in response to
Mr George's paper CEGB/P/10(ADD5).
April 1984. 7pp.

COUNSEL TO THE INQUIRY   CI/95(SAF)
Further notice by Counsel to the Inquiry for the cross-examination
of Dr Gittus (CEGB/P/16) (following CI/93).
May 1984. 3pp.

ICRP   CI/96(SAF)
Principles for Limiting Exposure of the Public to Natural Sources
of Radiation.
Statement from the 1983 Washington meeting of the ICRP. 1983.
(Extract).

COUNSEL TO THE INQUIRY   CI/97(GEN)
Early notice by Counsel to the Inquiry for cross-examination of
Mr Baker (CEGB/P46).
May 1984. 1p.

DANIELS, B K   CI/98(SAF)
Learning from experience.
(IN High Risk Safety Technology. Green, A E (Ed).
John Wiley and Sons Ltd. 1982. pp259-291.)

HOOKWAY, B R   CI/99(SAF)
Letter of 21 September 1983 from B R Hookway, Dept of the
Environment, to R B Pepper, CEGB, about the clarification
of the ALARA principle. 3pp.

DEPARTMENT OF THE ENVIRONMENT/CEGB   CI/99(ADD1)
Correspondence between B R Hookway, DOE, and R B Pepper, CEGB,
dated 31 October 1983 and 1 November 1983, and J P H Hood, CEGB,
to J Hannaford, NII, dated 25 May 1983. 8pp.

BRUNE, R L   CI/100(SAF)
Checklist for evaluating emergency operating procedures used in
nuclear power plants.
USNRC, NUREG/CR-2005(REV1).
Sandia National Laboratories, April 1983. (Extract).

PAPWORTH, D and VENNART, J   CI/101(SAF)
Radiation-induced leukaemia in spondylitics: dose response
relationships.
(IN British Medical Journal, Vol 285, 17 July 1982. p209-210.)

COUNSEL TO THE INQUIRY   CI/102(SAF)
Response to NNC/P/2(ADD2) to indicate the NNC and CEGB those areas
in which imcomplete answers appear to be provided in reply to
written questions asked by Counsel to the Inquiry and listed in
NNC/P/2(ADD2).
June 1984. 10pp.

COUNSEL TO THE INQUIRY   CI/103(NE)
Notice of scope of cross-examination of Mr Jenkins (CEGB) by
Counsel to the Inquiry on the work of the Cambridge Energy
Research Group and related matters.
June 1984. 4pp.

COUNSEL TO THE INQUIRY   CI/103(ADD1)
A note to be used for cross-examination purposes which brings
together into one place some of the concepts and figures which
are discussed in CEGB/P/4(ADD14 and 16).
June 1984. 2pp.

LANHAM, R A   CI/104(SAF)
Letter of 4 June 1984 from R A Lanham, GLC, to Inquiry Secretariat
about the proof of evidence of Prof T A Kletz. 3pp.

COUNSEL TO THE INQUIRY   CI/105(GEN)
Extracts from the Charter of the United Nations and the Statute of
the International Court of Justice.
11 June 1984. 3pp.

COUNSEL TO THE INQUIRY   CI/106(SAF)
Early notice by Counsel to the Inquiry for cross-examination of
Mr Miller (SSEB/P/1).
June 1984. 10pp.

COUNSEL TO THE INQUIRY   CI/106(ADD1)
Further notice by Counsel to the Inquiry for cross-examination
of Mr Miller (SSEB/P/1).
20 June 1984. 2pp.

KELLY, A   CI/107(NE)
Maintenance Planning and Control.
Butterworth & Co. 1984. (Extract). (ISBN 0 408 01375 3).

COUNSEL TO THE INQUIRY   CI/108(NE)
Meeting on ERG Model - 10 October 1983.
CI, 25 June 1984. 28pp.

COUNSEL TO THE INQUIRY   CI/109(NE)
OPEC in the world oil market in the 1980's.
(IN The Energy Crisis: Ten Years After. Howden, D (Ed).
London. Croon Helm, 1984. pp37-47.)

COUNSEL TO THE INQUIRY   CI/110(SAF)
Radiation exposure resulting from the normal transport of radiation
materials within the United Kingdom.
NRPB-R155. February 1984. 48pp; appendices.
(ISBN 0 85951 214 2).

COUNSEL TO THE INQUIRY   CI/111(SAF)
Emergency arrangements: Procedure for examination of efficacy.
CI, 2 August 1984. 1p.

COUNSEL TO THE INQUIRY   CI/111(ADD1)
Addendum to "Emergency arrangements: Procedure for examination
of efficacy.   .
CI, August 1984. 1p.

COUNSEL TO THE INQUIRY   CI/112(SAF)
The diffusion of responsibility in issues involving radiation
hazards. Advance notice to cross-examine: NRPB/P/1, DOE/P/2,
MAFF/P/2, NII/P/2 and DTp/P/1.
CI, August 1984. 1p.

COUNSEL TO THE INQUIRY   CI/113(SAF)
Advance notice to cross-examine Mr Pugh (NNC/P/1).
August 1984. 1p.

COUNSEL TO THE INQUIRY   CI/114(SAF)
Advance notice to cross-examine Mr Anthony (NII/P/1).
August 1984. 5pp.

COUNSEL TO THE INQUIRY   CI/114(ADD1)
Further notice to cross-examine Mr. Anthony (NII/P/1) by Counsel
to the Inquiry.   October 1984.   1 p.

COUNSEL TO THE INQUIRY   CI/115(SAF)
Notice to cross-examine Rosalie Bertell (SSBA/P/8) by Counsel to
the Inquiry.   12 September, 1984.   4 pp.

NATIONAL RADIOLOGICAL PROTECTION BOARD   CI/116(SAF)
Radiological Protection Bulletin.   No. 59.   July, 1984. (Extract)
(ISSN 0308-4272)

INTERNATIONAL COMMISSION ON RADIOLOGICAL PROTECTION   CI/117(SAF)
Report of Committee II on permissible dose for internal radiation.
KRP Publication 2.   Pergamon Press.   1959.   (Extract)

INTERNATIONAL COMMISSION ON RADIOLOGICAL PROTECTION   CI/118(SAF)
Limits for inhalation of radon daughters by workers.   ICRP Publication
No. 32.   Vol. 6.   No. 1.   Pergamon Press.   1981.   24 pp. inc.
appendices.

COUNSEL TO THE INQUIRY   CI/119(SAF)
Various estimates of the ratio - uncontrolled releases due to
aircraft crash/uncontrolled releases due to plant faults.   CI.
September, 1984.   1 p.

COUNSEL TO THE INQUIRY   CI/120(SAF)
Advance notice to cross-examine Mr. R. Anthony (NII/P/1) on policy
questions concerning emergency arrangements.   September, 1984.   3 pp.

COUNSEL TO THE INQUIRY   CI/121(SAF)
Answers to two questions raised by the NII arising out of CI documents
CI/93 (ADD 2), CI/112 placed before the Inquiry by Mr. H. Brooke
on the 3 August, 1984.   September, 1984.   4 pp.

COUNSEL TO THE INQUIRY   CI/122(SAF)
Notice to the National Radiological Protection Board.
(Dr. Clarke, NRPB/P/1) by Counsel to the Inquiry.   October, 1984.
1 p.

COUNSEL TO THE INQUIRY   CI/123(SAF)
Notice to cross-examine Mr. Critchley (DOE/P/1) by Counsel to the
Inquiry.   October, 1984.   2 pp.

COUNSEL TO THE INQUIRY   CI/124(SAF)
Further notice to cross-examine Mr. Pugh (NNC/P/2) by Counsel to
the Inquiry (see CI/113).   October, 1984.   2 pp.

COUNSEL TO THE INQUIRY   CI/124(ADD1)
Further notice to cross-examine Mr. Pugh (NNC/P/1 and NNC/P/2) by
Counsel to the Inquiry (see also CI/113 and CI/124).
14 November, 1984.   3 pp.

COUNSEL TO THE INQUIRY   CI/125(SAF)
Advance notice to cross-examine Mr. A. R. Gregory (CEGB/P/24).
9 October 1984.   1 p.

NRPB   CI/126(SAF)
Radiological protection objectives for the disposal of solid
radioactive wastes.   NRPB - GS1.   October 1983.   10 pp.

DRYE, D. J.   CI/127(SAF)
Letter of 7 October 1984 from D. J. Drye to Mr. Brooke, Counsel to
the Inquiry, in connection with questions to Dr. D. G. Avery
(BNFL/P/1).   17 October 1984.   3 pp.

COUNSEL TO THE INQUIRY   CI/128(SAF)
High level waste - quantities.   October 1984.   4 pp.

CHUDLEIGH, R. and CANNELL, W.   CI/129(SAF)
Radioactive waste: the gravediggers dilemma.   Friends of the
Earth.   1984.   (Extract).   (ISBN 0 905966 33 3).

OTAKE, M. and SCHULL, W. J.   CI/130(SAF)
In utero exposure to A-bomb radiation and mental retardation:
a reassessment.   (In The British Journal of Radiology.
May 1984.   Vol. 57.   pp. 409-414.)

SPENCER, K.   CI/131(SAF)
Letter of 21 October 1984 from K. Spencer to Counsel to the Inquiry
about cross-examination of Mr. Peterken (GLC/P/11).   1 p.

HOUSE OF LORDS: SELECT COMMITTEE ON THE   CI/132(GEN)
EUROPEAN COMMUNITIES
European Community energy strategy and objectives.   Select
Committee on the European Communities 17th Report, with minutes of
evidence.   Session 1983-84.   London: HMSO.   1984.
(Extract) (HL 208)

ORDNANCE SURVEY   CI/133(GEN)
Saxmundham and Aldeburgh.   Sheet 156.   Landranger Series of
Great Britain.   1:50,000.   1981.   One map.

COUNSEL TO THE INQUIRY   CI/134(SAF)
Note for cross-examination of CND witnesses.   November, 1984.
4 pp.

COUNSEL TO THE INQUIRY   CI/135(ENV)
Written questions by Counsel to the Inquiry to Mr. Hare (WS/R/94).
November, 1984.   2 pp.

COUNSEL TO THE INQUIRY   CI/136(SAF)
Notice to cross-examine Dr. Alice Stewart (SSBA/P/7) by Counsel
to the Inquiry.   November, 1984.   2 pp.

COUNSEL TO THE INQUIRY   CI/137(NE)
Written questions by Counsel to the Inquiry to Local Planning
Authorities on LPA/P/1(ADD 2), and LPA/S/179.   November, 1984.
2 pp.

COUNSEL TO THE INQUIRY   CI/138(GEN)
Correspondence between Sir Charles Court, and Inquiry Secretariat
arising out of Day 223 (pages 43-72) in relation to evidence given
by Ms Flick on behalf of the Joint Ecology Parties.
12 December 1984.   4 pp.

COUNSEL TO THE INQUIRY   CI/139(SAF)
In Utero exposure to A-bomb irradiation and mental retardation:
a reassessment by Otake and Schull (CI/130).   14 December 1984.
1 p.

COUNSEL TO THE INQUIRY   CI/140(SAF)
Notice to cross-examine Mr. Woods NII/P/2 (ADD 18) and Mr. George
CEGB/P/10 (ADD 16).   19 December 1984.   11 pp.

Printed in the UK for HMSO by Bemrose Security Printing, Derby
Dd 239525 C 2.5 1/87